THE SOOTHING ART OF

Baby Massage

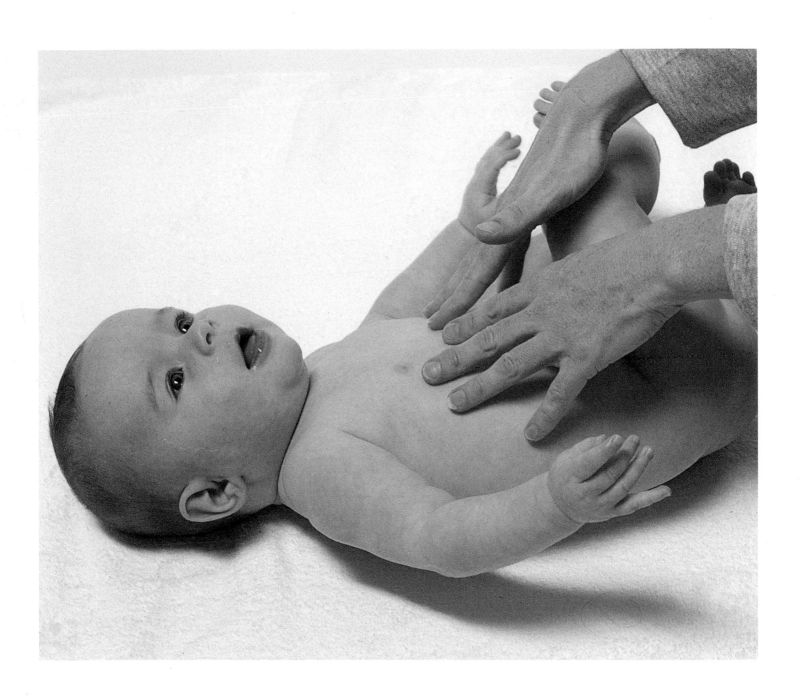

THE SOOTHING ART OF

Baby Massage

CHANCELLOR
PRESS

Contents

Chapter One

THE ART OF BABY MASSAGE   6

The Art of Baby Massage

When mothers massage their babies,
the massage assists the bonding process and helps establish a warm
and positive parent-child relationship.

The instinctive reaction to any physical trauma is to rub the sore spot. This indicates that massage was one of the first healing techniques used by humans. Throughout the centuries many different types of massage have been developed in response to the manifold aspects of well-being they bring.

As massage played such an important role in the care of adult bodies, so too was it extensively used to develop happy, healthy infants. The aristocrats of early Rome employed Greek slave girls as wet nurses for their babies. These slaves were often well-educated with a strong understanding of the benefits of massage in promoting tranquility in the babies under their care. Caring for babies by massage has been sustained for centuries.

Massage is communication at the deepest level, without the limitation of words. Fluid flow through the body is increased by massage. The improved blood flow benefits the nutrition and detoxification of the body's systems, while improved lymphatic flow enhances the efficiency of the immune system.

In babies, strong healthy growth is supported by the movement of fluids which provide nutrition to all cells and also assist the baby's excretory system. Massage is valuable in stimulating the sensory receptors in the skin and the layers below it. These stimulations increase the efficiency of the baby's nervous system.

Beyond all physical benefits of massage are the tremendous waves of emotional and caring "oneness" which come from this loving contact.

When a baby is born, it comes from the dark, encapsulated security of the womb, in which it was gently rocked by warm amniotic fluid and lulled by the rhythmic beat of its mother's heart. Now the baby is confronted by bright light and a confusing melee of sensations. The known sounds of its mother's voice and her touch assist the newly born baby to feel secure and wanted.

Life in the womb is by no means silent and is sometimes even described as "noisy". Movements of the organs surrounding the womb are sonorous so the fetus is aware of sound from its early months. Pregnant women often play music to their unborn child, which depending on the type of music seems to have a calming effect on the fetus.

At birth the most developed of our senses are touch, hearing and smell and the skin is the strongest organ of touch. Within seconds babies can identify the scent of their own mother. Once breathing is established, gentle, confident touch, known voices and pleasant smells will assist the baby to relax and be ready to suckle. Infant studies have shown that touch, movement and sound stimulate the nerve pathways, speeding neurological growth. Weight gain is faster and cellular activity is increased along with improved endocrine functioning.

For massage to be beneficial for the baby, it does not have to begin and end with massaging the baby during its first year after birth.

In this book we look at massage for the mother during pregnancy and childbirth — of great benefit for both mother and baby — and the post-natal period; as well as massage for the newborn and older baby and through the child's early years.

Thus, massage can become a part of life — from pregnancy to birth, through the growing years, to parenthood of the next generation.

The gentle touch of baby massage promotes relaxation and encourages the baby's self-healing potential.

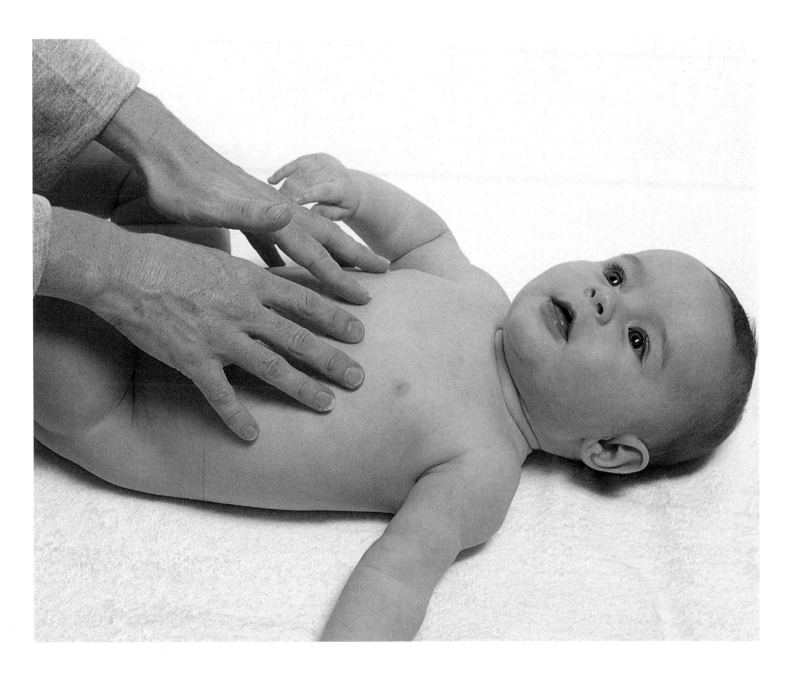

Birthing customs from around the world

There are great differences in attitudes to birth in various societies. In all societies there are those who assist at the actual birth. These may vary from a family member, friend or midwife to a general practitioner or obstetrician.

In the seventeenth century a few *accoucheurs* (male midwives) began to assist in the delivery of babies; however, midwifery was carried out predominantly by women. Gradually midwives became more accepted as practitioners in their own right, but were subordinate to doctors. Before 1880, most births were attended by female relatives, with a doctor called in at the last moment, if labor became difficult. From 1880–1920 many babies were born at home. After 1930 the medical profession exerted increased authority over the birth process and births more and more became medical events occurring in hospital. Though midwives increased in number and were given greater training, most modern midwives are attached to hospitals or community centers.

In the past fifty years, in modern Western societies, an increase in the number of successful births with improved baby health has been achieved. As women in the modern world became more educated and informed than their sisters of the past, they came to feel that the "hospitalization" of birth had unduly changed this normal, biological event into a medical one, in which the pregnant woman becomes a passive patient, to be instructed in what she is to do, or not to do. The trend now is for many women to be more "active" in the birth process.

Early in this century the body was being compared with a machine — the criticism leveled at some obstetricians is that they see the birth process only as one of plumbing. This narrow view does not include the complex emotional and psychological aspects of birth. Birth is a time of momentous change and emotional fulfilment for the new parents. Today we are seeing birthing options which sanction the woman's wishes regarding all aspects of birthing, whether the baby is born at home, in a birth center or in a hospital setting. As well, the male partner or other family members or a chosen support person are likely to be present and helping with the birth.

Views of birth in various parts of the world are often very different. In some cultures the placenta is viewed as dangerous to the males. To avoid contamination they stay away from the birth and often have no contact with the woman or the baby for the next month.

In many countries a woman rarely gives birth lying on her back in bed. In South East Asia, India, West Africa and in the Central Americas women stand, squat or sit, or recline against a support, while giving birth, and the cord is not cut until after the placenta has been expelled. It is usual in these societies for the mother to have a period of rest and seclusion lasting from twenty to forty days following the birth of a child.

In areas where traditional birthing takes place, "Traditional Birth Attendants" are the usual support persons. The term comes from the United Nations World Health Organization. WHO is actively working to increase the training of these people. Attitudes which allow women to keep their beliefs and mores intact, acknowledge the psychological and emotional aspects of childbirth, often overlooked or ignored in the past by the "hospitalized" approach to childbirth.

An approach which acknowledges the benefits of both modern medicine and traditional practices is developing in most Western countries. Modern lifestyle and clothing are not conducive to the way in which the baby is carried and cared for in the weeks after birth. In societies which still follow age-old traditions, the baby is constantly with the mother or a carer. A new mother's clothing is adapted to accommodate her infant. In West Africa, Indonesia and some of the islands of the Pacific, babies are placed in slings across their mothers' breasts. While in Indonesia the sling is a separate garment, some other indigenous women form a sling from their long skirts. There is much skin to skin contact and the baby has immediate access to its mother's breasts.

Many Western women have returned to "feeding on demand". Babies treated in this way are more likely to be happy and calm as crying to express discomfort or hunger is avoided. As indigenous mothers move about, babies supported close to their bodies in soft, pliant slings are constantly being massaged by the fabric and the movement of the mother's muscles. Compare this with the experience of most Western babies, who spend a considerable time lying in bassinets, cots or prams. As well as carrying their babies most of their working day, indigenous women from India, Central America, Uganda, and Fiji, among other islands in the Pacific, have specific times for planned baby massage. The lubricant varies according to the season or the baby's state of health.

In the Pacific islands, mothers massage their babies with coconut oil after the baby's daily bath. They use massage at night to help lull the baby to sleep.

Children brought up to enjoy and respond to soothing massage have a wonderful start to life. Early massaging implants the notion "rubbing it better" as a concept for treating trauma. This is a powerful alternative to the pill popping habits of modern society.

Life's most wonderful and important experiences are intangible. Although baby massage has proven benefits for the infant and for those doing the massaging, its values are immeasurable. Overlying the scientifically established benefits of touch, baby massaging develops bonding between the baby and its parents.

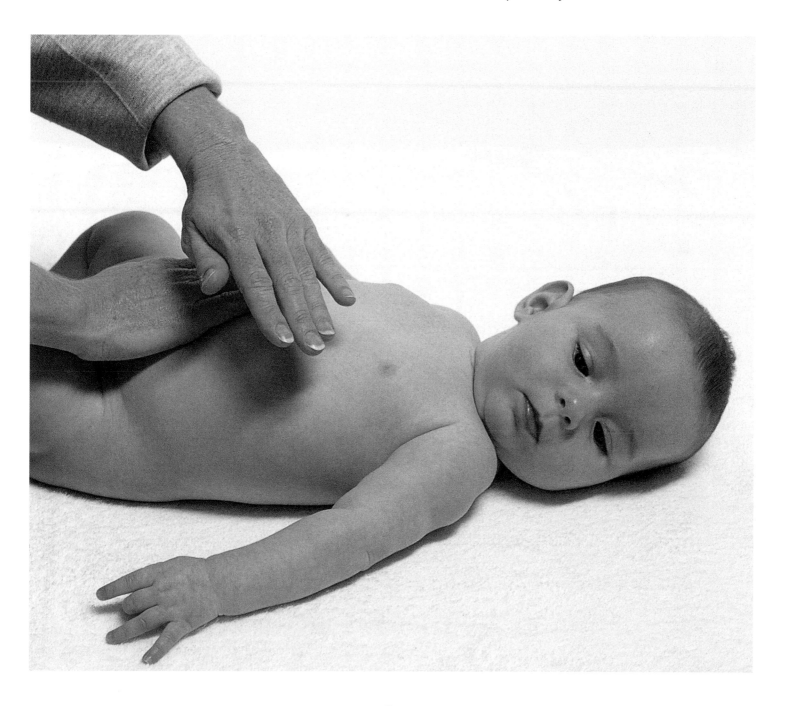

Health and physical benefits of baby massage

Massage is a conscious touch.
When a mother massages her newborn
infant she is focused
on the softness of her baby's skin;
she becomes aware
of the baby's fragility and vulnerability,
and of this vibrant
new life reaching out to her.

The baby was secure inside the womb. Once the baby arrives into the world, it misses this warmth and security; but then it feels the warmth of its mother's body, and bonding takes place. This is the time the baby needs its mother's closeness, her touch and the whisper of loving words for reassurance. Interchange of the energy of love between mother and infant comes through the closeness of skin contact, touch, communication through eye contact and the mother's voice.

But this happy scenario is not always the reality. When interviewed about their baby's birth, many mothers have stated that immediately after the birth they were so tired and overwhelmed by the hours of pain and effort, they didn't even want to see or hold the newborn child. Touch and simple massage can assist in overcoming these feelings.

Often when we touch something — even another human being — we are not consciously aware of the tactile sensation of what we are touching. *Massage is a conscious touch*. When a mother massages her newborn infant, she is focused on the softness of her baby's skin; she becomes aware of the baby's fragility and vulnerability, and of this vibrant new life reaching out to her. The joy and comfort these actions bring is a powerful means of conquering that terrible state of postnatal blues.

As an ongoing practice, baby massage encourages healthy growth and plays an important role in the physical and mental development of the baby. The baby's circulation and immune systems will improve; massage is also a healing technique which affects the physical, emotional and spiritual levels of the child.

Massage is not only beneficial for the baby, but also for the massage giver. It is a means of relief from stress and of generating bonding between parents, and parents and baby. Another benefit of massaging the baby is that it increases the massage giver's confidence in handling the baby.

A massage allows time
for the parent and baby
to become intimately
acquainted and so assists
the bonding process.

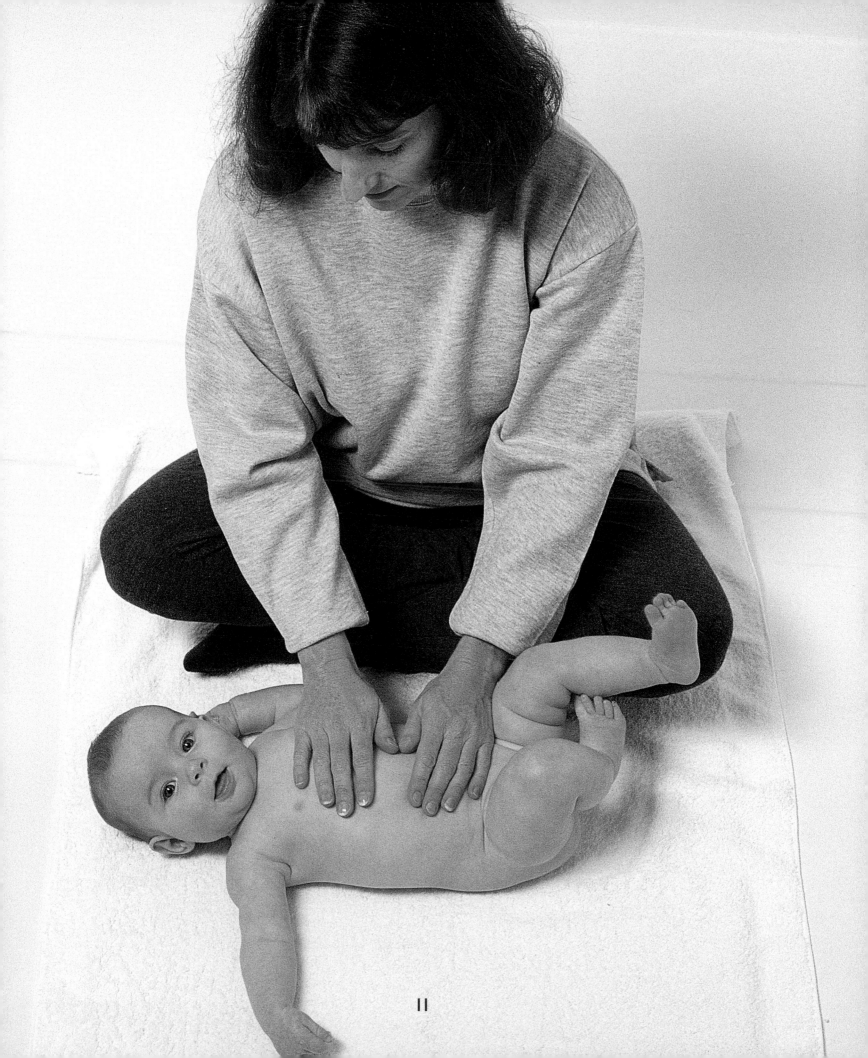

Preparation for baby's massage

In preparing to massage
your baby
consider the temperature
and atmosphere
of the room, the time of day,
and the oils
you wish to use.

Babies and small children respond to routine. The establishment of what will be the usual procedure helps develop feelings of security in the baby. Recognition of routines is the beginning of the baby's understanding of this strange, new world. The best time for baby massage is when the baby is neither tired nor hungry. Abdominal stroking should not be attempted too soon after a drink.

While massage is a message of warmth and love for the baby, beware of the child's responses becoming too demanding. As a survival mechanism, all young creatures are egocentric and occupied with their own needs and wants. Your bundle of joy can turn into a small tyrant if you allow too much control to transfer into your baby's hands. For instance, the constant rocking of a healthy baby may lead to an over demand for this activity.

Needs of other members of the household must be considered if the environment is to be a secure, happy one. Other children in the household, especially toddlers, must not be ignored because of the new baby. Often small children are delighted to "help" with the massage — possibly stroking the baby's hands or feet. This will teach the older child the necessary gentleness of touch.

The shared joy of touch and response strengthens bonding within families. Sometimes partners feel they are being left out and ignored if the mother's interests seem to be all oriented towards the baby. Involve your partner in massaging the baby too. They will love it and benefit from it and so will the baby.

*The best time to massage your baby is between feeds,
when the baby is neither hungry nor full.*

Creating the environment

To ensure your baby gains maximum benefit from the massage, give thought to preparing the best environment: warm, quiet and softly lit. Have your oils and other necessary items ready.

Make sure the area you choose is draft free, warm and with soft light, natural if possible. If there is a phone, take it off the hook or switch on the answering machine. This special time should be just for you and your baby.

Sit in a comfortable place, perhaps on a beanbag or a pile of cushions that you can lean into for support for your back. If you are going to massage your baby on the floor, lay out a padded mat or quilt. Have a towel under the baby in case of mishaps.

Some soft music playing in the background may help to create a calming atmosphere. Make sure there is no strong light, neither sunlight nor electric, shining on your baby's face. When the baby is face up, use a shaded side lamp, or soft natural light.

Getting ready

Make sure your fingernails are short and clean and all jewellery has been removed.

Have the baby's clothes and the oil at hand so you won't have to fetch items leaving the baby unattended. Unless you are breast feeding, have a bottle prepared before the massage. Depending on the time of the massage, babies often like a feed straight after their massage.

Toddlers can present a problem as they may not always choose to be massaged when you think the time appropriate. If they are accustomed to frequent massages from their earliest days, however, most toddlers will seek touch. When they fall or hurt themselves, they will want to be "rubbed better." Adapt the sequence described in the chapter on baby massage for your toddler, but gradually increase the pressure until you are working firmly up the limbs and only using the lightest pressure when moving down the limbs, thus you will work correctly with the flow of fluids through the body. If your toddler is impatient to be off and about the serious business of exploring and growing, do parts of the body at a time.

The oils

Use only cold pressed vegetable oils or seed oils such as sweet almond, olive oil or even grapeseed oil. Avoid heavy oils such as peanut oil. Also avoid commercial baby oil, which is a mineral oil specifically developed as a barrier to urine and will not be absorbed by the skin. The mineral content is not helpful to the child's skin, whereas sweet almond oil has an emollient effect. Do not apply the oil directly to the baby's skin; rather, put a small quantity on your hands to warm it before applying it to the baby.

Remember your baby has only a tiny body, with a limited blood supply, so if the weather is at all chilly, warm the oil slightly by standing the container in a bowl of warm water and keep the room warm. A squeeze bottle that can be used with one hand, is the easiest way of dispensing oil. Remember to replace the lid after essential oils have been added. A small sauce bottle from the supermarket is perfect. However, later on, when you are using essential oils, avoid plastic containers, as some oils erode plastic. Essential oils are concentrated, so they are not recommended for direct use on the newborn. They may be used as room sprays for improving the quality of the air in the home.

See the chapter on aromatherapy for further information on the care of essential oils.

Keep a favorite toy on hand to keep the environment familiar and cosy.

CAUTION

After an immunization session, your baby's temperature will be raised slightly. It is advised that you do not massage your baby for several days afterwards.

Basic massage movements

There are a number of basic techniques which are useful and easy to learn.

Especially when in contact with the first baby, many parents are tentative. However, the baby needs sureness of touch, so it is important for adults to be confident. Although small, and needing gentleness, healthy babies are not so fragile that they cannot be massaged. It is important for the massage giver to "tune in" to their own hands and the energy flow passing through them.

Before handling the baby, check that your fingernails are short and clean and that you have no rough cuticles or skin on your fingers. Warm your hands by bathing them in hot water. Dry them by vigorously rubbing them with a towel. This will increase circulation thereby ensuring warm hands. The fingertips are the most sensitive to touch, so use them to feel your baby, especially when checking for any sore spots.

The greatest energy flows through the palm of the hand. Place the whole hand on your baby wherever it will fit and concentrate on feeling the flow of energy from you to your baby, and from your baby back to you. This vital exchange of energies is one reason why both parties benefit so much from a massage.

Besides being aware of your fingertips and palms, you will need to adapt your grip and movements to fit the space. In some areas your massaging will be done with just a finger and thumb. Remember to follow your child's contours so that as much of your hand as possible is in touch with the skin.

Some of the basic movements and techniques used in baby massage are outlined here. After the confined space and curled fetal position, the aim of a baby massage is to "straighten" the baby to enable freedom of movement. This is done by working from the head to the toes and from the shoulder to the fingertips, encouraging the response of the baby. As you become accustomed to massaging your baby, you will no doubt incorporate many movements of your own. Massage is not a limited art.

You can expect your baby to join in the massage. The movements under your hands, and possibly sounds, will guide you in making the massage enjoyable. The process should be pleasurable and fun for you both.

Massage skills

This book will give you a glimpse into the extraordinary value of touch through massage. If you have never experienced the complete comfort of massage, contact a qualified practitioner in your area and see what a wonderful dimension massage can add to your life. Professional massage associations will be able to guide you in your choice and put you in touch with practitioners who have high levels of ability, caring and ethics. Many practitioners use essential oils for aromatherapy massage.

If you find you have an interest in honing and extending the skills you have developed at home there are massage courses available. And while increasing your massage skills, consider exploring ways of expanding your knowledge of essential oils.

If practiced regularly, you will find that massaging your baby will become intuitive. It is not the technique as such that is all important so much as the warmth of human contact and your relationship with your child. Without trust and affection, techniques will be merely mechanical routines.

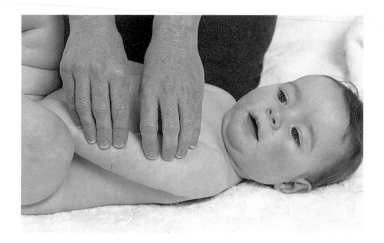

Fingertip pressure

Using the pads of your fingers (take care to avoid using the nails), very light fingertip pressures are a useful way to begin massage on a small baby. Press gently on the shoulders, then move downwards, progressing only a short distance with each press. After working from the shoulders down the body, progress onto the arms and then the legs, where the pressure can still be light, but a little firmer than it was on the body. This technique promotes circulation.

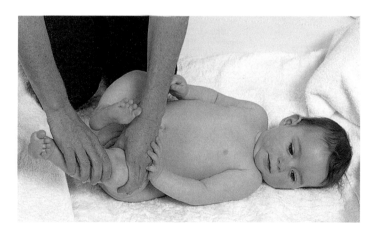

Gentle squeezing

Each squeeze is achieved by curling the fingers around the arm or leg and contracting it towards the thumb. After releasing the pressure, slide the hand to the next area not yet touched and squeeze again. Progress in this way down the arms and then the legs. After each downward movement, lightly slide back to the shoulder or thigh and repeat the process several times.

Effleurage

Given a baby to hold, nearly everyone will instinctively stroke. "Effleurage" is the massage term for stroking forward then back in the opposite direction. It is generally a soothing, smoothly flowing stroke applied with gentle but firm pressure. This is a movement which comes naturally to most people. Pay attention to how the hand is cupped or flattened to stay in maximum contact with the contours of the area being massaged. Most of the baby massage will be some form of gentle stroking. Partners and family members can easily become involved in this stroking. The gentle movement expresses the caring love from the massage giver to the baby. At the same time the neurological response is being stimulated.

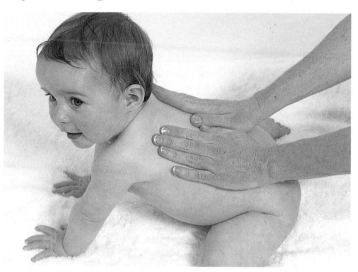

As a baby's body is so small, you will probably use the stroking movements most often. Most of the baby massage will be some form of gentle stroking.

Draining

Draining the tissues is an important technique in massage, and is often used in the abdominal region. Most of the body is abundantly supplied with microcopic lymphatic vessels. Even the lightest stroking can encourage the lymphatic fluid to move through these minute tubes, while firmer pressure can assist the flow back to the heart. The lymphatic system is vital for our immunity to infections.

Place the hand on the relevant part of the body and, while moving it along the skin, gently press the palm or the fingertips through the tissues.

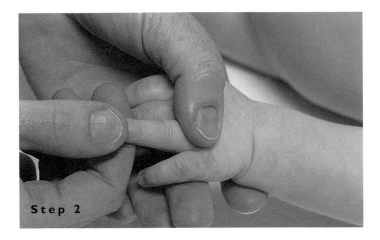

Step 2

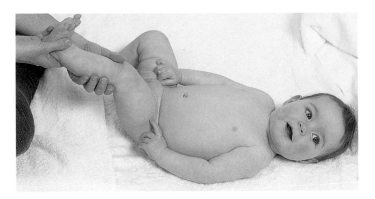

Stretching

Stretching must begin smoothly and be gentle in the amount of traction used. At all times, the person massaging needs to be sensitive to the responses of the infant and to the feel of the joints. Smoothness and gentle firmness are required. The movement must not be sudden or jerky, nor should it be too "feathery" light as this could cause irritation.

Finger rotation

1. Using your thumbs, or the palms of your hand, with your fingers sliding on the back of your baby's hand, stroke down towards the fingertips. You may not find it easy to do this, but gently persevere because opening and stretching of the hands is important for the development of your baby's future tactile skills.

2. Beginning with the little finger of the left hand, using your own finger and thumb, stroke downwards. Hold your position on the finger and lean back to exert a slight traction to the finger. Use your body weight, not the muscles of your hands and arms.

3. Now roll your baby's finger with your hand and rotate the metacarpal joint (at the base of the finger).

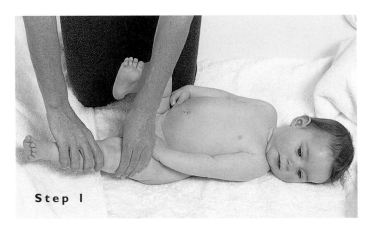

Step 1

Kneading

1. Kneading is taking the flesh in one hand, squeezing it and then grasping the held part with the other hand, to do an "S" shaped rolling squeeze. Continue changing from hand to hand. This "grasping, squeezing and releasing" moves the tissues from hand to hand, removing toxins and debris from the cells, while carrying nutrients to the whole body. This is often likened to kneading dough and is a gentle action.

2. On babies it may be necessary to use only two fingers and a thumb of each hand when kneading thighs, arms or buttocks, though on the thighs there may be room for full hands. With practice you will soon develop skills that are uniquely appropriate for you and your hands.

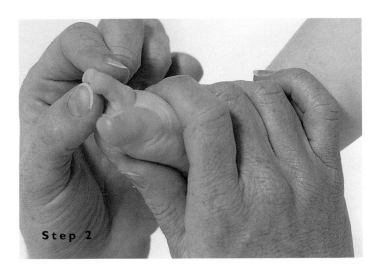

Step 2

Toe rotation

Beginning with the smallet toe, follow the instructions for finger rotation.

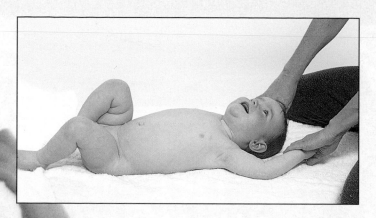

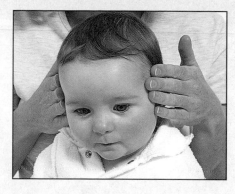

Frictions

Small circular movements made with the pads of the thumbs or fingers are called frictions. Use this massage movement to work on areas that feel tight, because it works at a deeper level. Frictions are designed to penetrate tension buildup.

Passive movement for the arms

After massaging the arms and hands hold the baby's wrists and lift the arms above the head. The degree of movement must be natural and not be forced in any way. Having reached the extension that is comfortable, hold the stretch for five to ten seconds. This movement improves flexibility of the shoulder joints. It also raises the diaphragm and enlarges the rib cage. Besides being vital to breathing, the diaphragm is the main muscle of the lymphatic system. This stretch will aid the movement of lymphatic fluid up through the thoracic duct leading to its return to the heart, thus improving the capacity of the immune response.

Much of the value of *touch* is intangible. Just holding a tiny baby (or any human or animal) gives the holder the opportunity to allow their energy to flow into the held. Although difficult to define in words, the therapeutic, magical effect of touch is unlimited, giving security and love to the one touched, held, or massaged — and joy to the giver.

Always begin with gentle movements, increasing the pressure as you feel the muscle tissue softening.

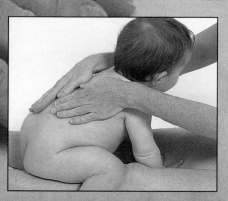

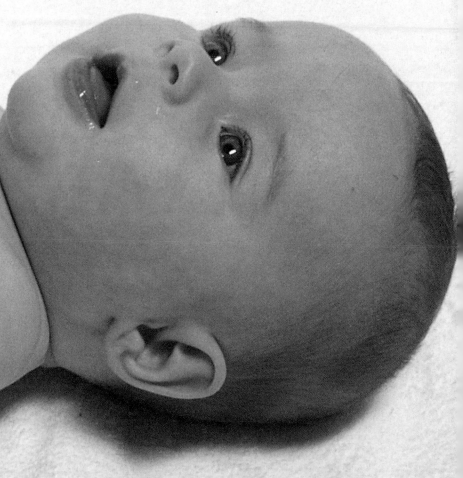

Energy exchange

Sometimes called massaging the "aura" or the electrical field, this movement could begin a massage, end a massage, or be of benefit at any stage. It is especially so of massage around the head of a frail or premature baby. It is done by forming small circles in the air close to the skin — not on it. Our nervous systems are electrochemical. Beyond the skin, we all have an electromagnetic field, the stroking of which may be of great comfort to a newborn who has experienced a difficult birth. After this light stroking *off* the skin, as the days pass your baby will accept stroking (effleurage) *on* the skin.

Massage During Pregnancy

While the woman's partner massages her abdomen,
they both have the pleasure of feeling the baby's first kick, feeling its limbs
and observing the baby's development by touch.

When your pregnancy is confirmed, you should give thought to where the birth will take place and make plans for the event. Inquire about prenatal clinics and the availability of information for pregnancy.

During the first three months of pregnancy all medication should be avoided, unless prescribed by your doctor. Significant attention should be paid to diet, exercise and sleep. Gentle massage may help prevent stretch marks and maintain an overall optimum quality of health.

The hormone progesterone helps the body soften and accommodate the growing baby. Muscles and ligaments are stretching, while the softening blood vessels are carrying twice as much blood as normal. All these changes have an effect on the body which may cause minor ailments, such as backache, nausea, vomiting, hemorrhoids, varicose veins, or edema (swelling) of the legs and feet. Massage and the use of essential oils may help to relieve these common complaints and are also beneficial for relieving other conditions, such as headaches, heartburn and insomnia, that can often occur during pregnancy. Aromatherapy during pregnancy is especially useful as at this time your sense of smell will be more acute. This is one of nature's ways of helping you to preserve your health and that of your fetus, as many dangerous substances will be unpleasant to your sense of smell. For more information on using massage and essential oils for these common pregnancy ailments, see the chapter on aromatherapy.

Because of the hormonal changes, your moods may not be as stable as usual but may vary unexpectedly. To maintain your health and your baby's, make sure your diet includes large amounts of fresh vegetables and fruits. If possible, take eight glasses of water daily, in addition to other fluid intake. Attend to the protein content of your meals. Your baby's bones and tissues need protein for growth. Fish, poultry, grains, lentils, legumes, nuts, dairy products, and meat are sources of protein. If you are unsure of your diet seek help. Eat a wide variety of foods so that the dietary needs of both you and your baby are met.

If you use substances that could affect your developing baby (alcohol, cigarettes, medications, drugs, etc.), stop, or at least reduce their use while you are pregnant. If you are planning well in advance for a baby, stop harmful habits at least three months before conception.

Exercise should be according to your lifestyle and experience, but should be carried out frequently. Walking and swimming are good prenatal exercises and there are many special exercise classes offered for pregnant women. Adequate rest and fresh air contribute to a healthy body, especially required in pregnancy. As the time passes, inquire about the availability of prenatal classes, where one can receive a wealth of information about childbirth. Join a relaxation class. The skills you learn in these classes are important when you are in labor. If you have any questions, or fears, jot them down in a notebook so you will not forget to ask them during your next prenatal visit.

From the second trimester, abdominal massage is an excellent way for you to get to know your baby. Not only the mother to be, but her partner will also benefit practicing this massage by feeling the growing baby. Both mother and father then have the pleasure of feeling their baby's first kick, feeling its limbs and observing their baby's development by touch.

The parental touch can be experienced by the baby in the womb. An overactive baby can be calmed by massage. This has been repeatedly tested. An active baby's heartbeat is monitored by a cardiotocograph machine. While on the CTG, a gentle massage calms the baby and still maintains a good "variable" heartbeat, which is medically correct at this stage of development.

*Abdominal massage can be
experienced by the baby in the womb.
An overactive baby
can be calmed by massage.*

If you are having your baby in hospital, or in a birthing center, it is advisable, in advance, to go and see the place to familiarize yourself with it and to meet the midwives. Then, when the time comes, you will know exactly where to go and what to do. If you wish to use massage and essential oils during your labor, make sure you discuss it with the doctor or the midwives at the hospital. Near the time of birth, in the last three to four weeks, have your bag packed and ready with things you would like to take for the birth: toiletries, nightwear, oils, and clothes in which to bring the baby home.

Perineal massage

The perineum is the area between the vagina and the anus. It will thin out and stretch during the birth of the baby. In some cases, however, it may not stretch enough and tears can occur. Perineal massage can reduce the risk of this tearing. The massage needs to be practiced daily for 5 to 10 minutes from 6 weeks prior to your delivery. Massaging the area can also help you to relax during vaginal examinations.

A suitable time for this massage is following a warm bath to increase circulation and soften the tissues. Do not have long fingernails, and wash your hands thoroughly. Ensure that your bladder is empty and sit in a comfortable position.

Using a mirror to make sure the oil is being applied in the right area, massage sweet almond oil (or wheatgerm or vitamin E oil if you have previous scarring) onto the perineum. Place your thumb inside the vagina and gently press towards the anus. Maintain steady pressure and massage gently and firmly back and forth over the lower wall of the vagina in a "U" shape, working the oil well into the outside of the perineal tissues. Keep stretching until you feel a slight burning, tingling or stinging sensation. (This is what you will experience when the baby's head is emerging.) The vagina should be stretched for 30 to 60 seconds and then released.

Stretch marks

A gentle daily massage on the stomach, breasts and hips will help keep the skin supple. Try a blend of 5 drops lavender and 2 drops neroli in 1 oz (30 mls) of base carrier oil such as sweet almond oil and use about a teaspoonful for each massage. Add wheatgerm oil, evening primrose oil or vitamin E oil (to make up 10% of the total blend) for added skin nourishment. Other recommended essential oils for preventing stretchmarks are frankincense and rose, and hypericum and calendula. Remember to use a clockwise movement when applying the oil to the abdomen.

If you are pregnant and would like to be massaged,
check with your doctor or midwife before proceeding.

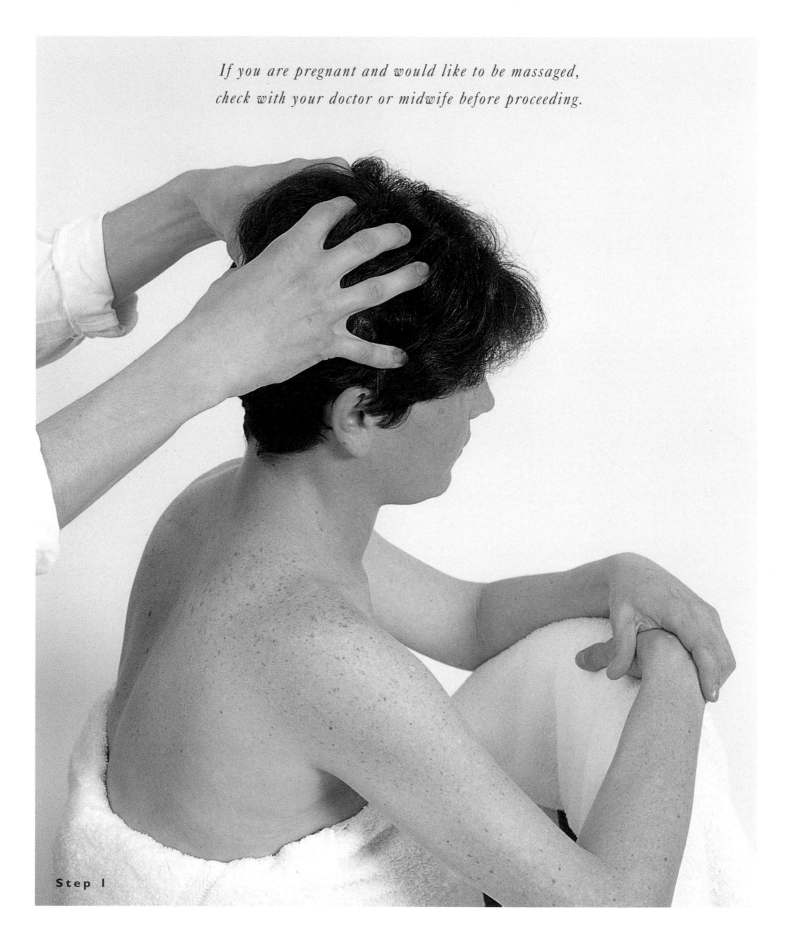

Step 1

Here are some effective massage strokes your partner may perform on you to ease your discomfort or tension or merely for your relaxation and enjoyment. The instructions are addressed to your partner.

Head and neck massage

1. This may be done while the pregnant woman is sitting upright in a chair, or in any other comfortable position. Stand behind her and gently stroke her head, then massage by holding your fingers still, while moving the scalp smoothly and evenly over the skull. Move your fingers a slight distance and keep working in tiny circles with your fingers until you've covered the head. Remember to concentrate on moving the scalp, not just your fingers. These movements release tension and increase circulation.

2. Slide one hand down the neck while supporting the forehead with the other hand. Massage the neck muscles with your fingers and thumb.

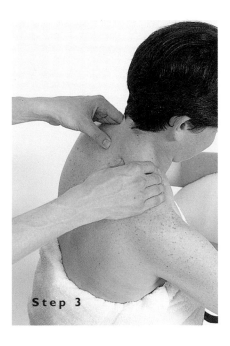

Step 3

3. Effleurage (stroke) around the shoulder area. Using both hands, one on either side of the neck, knead along the shoulder muscles by rolling your fingers towards your thumbs, as you slide sideways. Sustain an even pressure as you work sideways. As well as rolling the muscles towards you, slightly stretch the muscles towards the shoulders. Squeezing, rolling, lifting and stretching will remove toxins and improve nutrition in the tissues. This movement is a combination of kneading and draining.

Back massage

During pregnancy a woman's back takes a lot of strain due to the change in the center of gravity. Back massage will help relieve the discomfort. A warm shower or bath, prior to the massage, will be an added bonus.

1. Position your partner on a bean bag or on the side of the bed with a chair supporting her legs. Using a blend containing lavender oil, move in sweeping effleurage (stroking movements) over her back, starting at the gluteals (buttocks) and fanning upwards.

2. Slide your hands gently back to the gluteals allowing your hands to follow the body's contours.

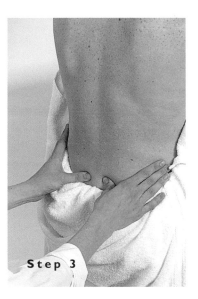

Step 3

3. As shown, use your fingers to move the flesh over the thumbs in a roll. Keep the pressure on the thumbs as you move upwards. The work must be gentle but even. This sliding and kneading (often called "crab walk") from the gluteals to the shoulders helps to drain waste products, relieving congestion in the tissues and helping to cleanse the body.

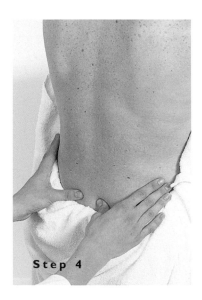

Step 4

4. Place both hands at the base of the spine and, using your body weight to keep even control of your pressure, use a fanning out movement from the coccyx to the top of the hips. After each upward move, let your hands slide around the gluteals back to the coccyx. Repeat these movements to help strengthen the back muscles.

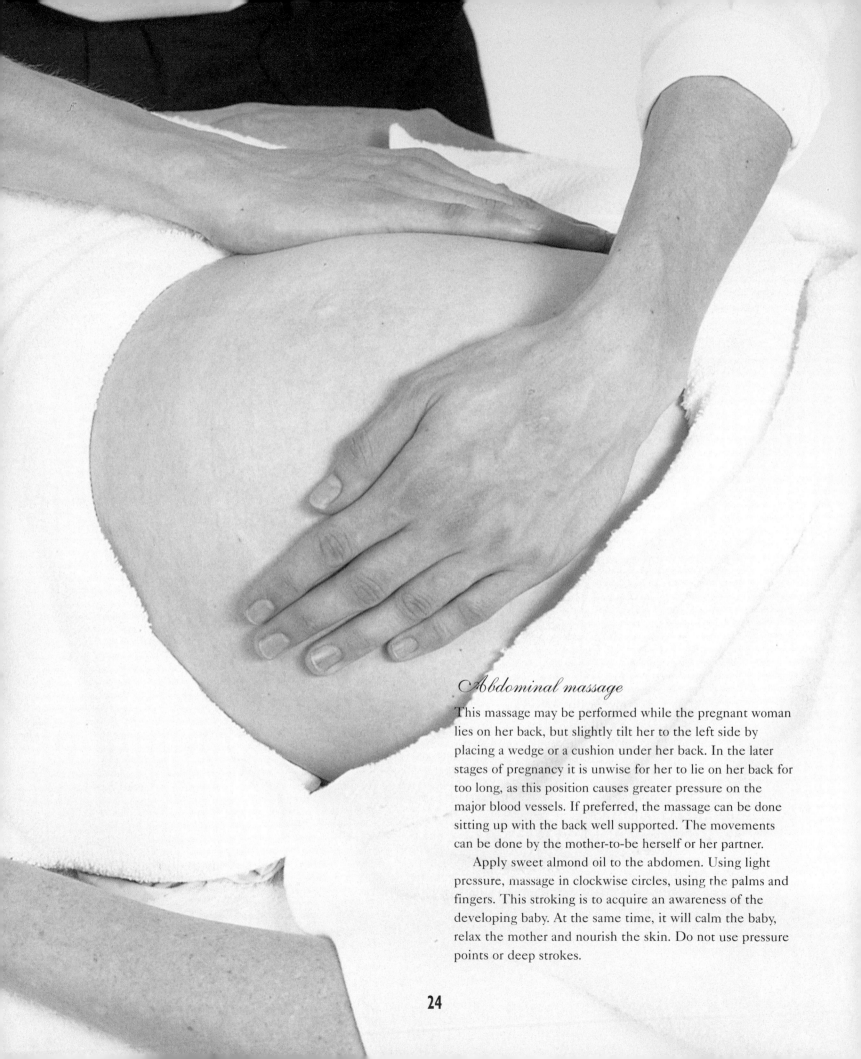

Abdominal massage

This massage may be performed while the pregnant woman lies on her back, but slightly tilt her to the left side by placing a wedge or a cushion under her back. In the later stages of pregnancy it is unwise for her to lie on her back for too long, as this position causes greater pressure on the major blood vessels. If preferred, the massage can be done sitting up with the back well supported. The movements can be done by the mother-to-be herself or her partner.

Apply sweet almond oil to the abdomen. Using light pressure, massage in clockwise circles, using the palms and fingers. This stroking is to acquire an awareness of the developing baby. At the same time, it will calm the baby, relax the mother and nourish the skin. Do not use pressure points or deep strokes.

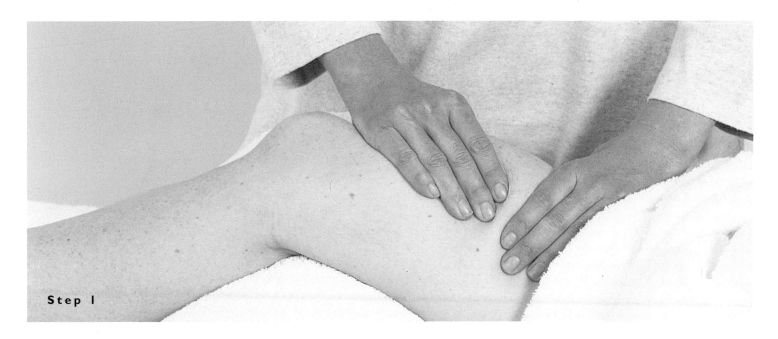

Step 1

Leg massage

Not only for pregnant women, but for anyone with tired feet, this massage is relaxing and soothing. It may be done while sitting up or lying on a table or massage bench or on a bed.

1. Stand at the foot of the bed and apply the oil upwards to your partner's thighs with an effleurage movement.

2. Slide your hands over the ankle, then hold the foot firmly with one hand. With the other hand massage the ankle with circular strokes, applying the pads of the fingers and of the thumb. Gently rotate the ankle to help relieve any fluid retention. Avoid massaging legs with varicose veins as this may aggravate the condition. Do not apply pressure to the back of the knees, to avoid damage to blood vessels and nerves.

3. Using both hands and keeping the movements continuous, circle the knee with your fingertips.

4. Work up to the thighs and knead them, to drain wastes from the muscles and to ease painful spasms.

When massaging a pregnant woman, avoid deep pressure and keep the movements smooth.

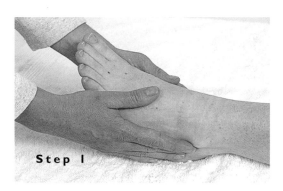

Step 1

Foot massage

It is important when attending to the feet that the touch is firm. If it is too light, it may cause distress to your partner, especially if she is ticklish.

Blend 2 drops of lavender with 2 drops of sandalwood in 2 teaspoons (10 ml) of carrier oil to use on the feet.

1. Cup your fingers around the sole of the left foot, and massage all of it. Move the bones (metatarsals) by holding the sole with your fingers and placing your thumbs parallel on top of the foot. Start on the little toe side and gently move each metatarsal up and down as you work across the foot. Suppleness of the feet assists in a feeling of well-being.

2. Gently rotate the ankle.

3. Massage the toes by gripping them one at a time, then squeezing and giving a moderate stretch. Repeat several times.

4. Repeat on the right foot.

Massage During Childbirth

A partner's involvement in massaging can provide valuable support and reassurance for a woman in labor. Relaxation increases natural pain relief by releasing endorphins. This in turn increases energy and reduces stress.

Before you go into labor, you may have had a few false starts. When the real thing happens you will have regular contractions. Your abdomen will go hard for forty to sixty seconds, then it will return to its original soft state. These contractions will resemble menstrual twinges to begin with. Usually, they will come every thirty minutes, gradually increasing to every five to ten minutes. When they are regular at this interval phone your midwife or hospital to let them know you are on your way. They will advise you what to do. If your waters have broken or if you have any bleeding let your midwife know immediately.

Massage during childbirth can be of immeasurable value; it can relax you, relieve backache, and help you feel more comfortable, calm and reassured. Once labor is established, and contractions are regular, showers or baths are also useful in alleviating stress and pain.

Preparation using essential oils

Prepare the birthing room by burning lavender and tangerine oils. As labor progresses, this may be changed to an oil of your choice. It is wonderful to welcome a baby to a scented atmosphere. If you do not have an oil burner or vaporizer, use a bowl of hot water with a few drops of essential oils to achieve similar results. See the chapter on aromatherapy for more information.

While you are in labor, a partner's involvement in massaging can provide valuable support and reassurance for you. Relaxation increases natural pain relief by releasing endorphins. This in turn increases energy and reduces stress. When massaging, it is important for you both to be in a comfortable position.

The instructions for the following massage sequence are addressed to the pregnant woman's partner.

Step 1

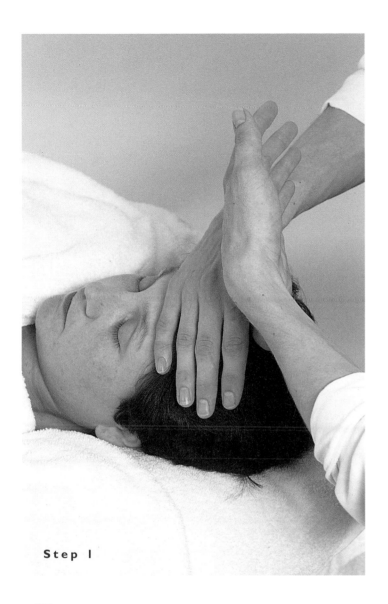

Step 1

Face massage

Most women do not like their face being massaged during labor, but your partner may tolerate a gentle stroking over her forehead between contractions.

1. Apply a little oil on your hands, warm them by rubbing them together and, using the palms, stroke her forehead smoothly and gently, one hand after the other, to ease anxiety.

2. During summer months, a face cloth soaked in lavender water and laid lightly across the forehead is cooling. Rosewater sprayed on the face between contractions has a soothing, calming effect on women in labor.

Back massage

1. As labor progresses, massage the shoulders.

2. At times when the baby is lying back to back (posterior position) it will help the mother to get on her hands and knees and rock her hips. This will help the baby move from that position and relieve your partner's backache.

Step 3

3. Before massaging your partner's back, she should be positioned on a bean bag or on the side of the bed with her legs supported on a chair. Begin at the coccyx (tail bone).

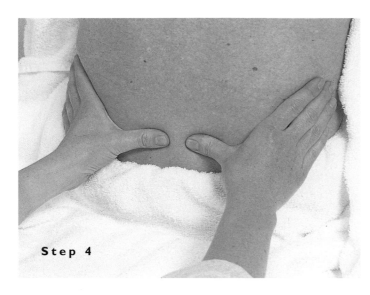

Step 4

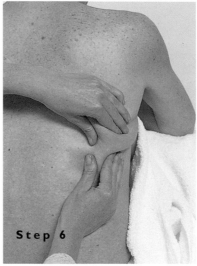

Step 6

6. Now move up the left side of the body rolling the flesh with your fingertips towards your thumbs. Continue to the shoulder. Repeat this movement on the right side of the body.

4. With your thumbs on either side of your partner's spine, make deep circles from the coccyx to the center of her back.

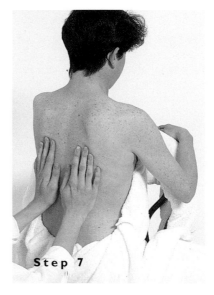

Step 7

7. With steady, firm pressure slide up and down the back from the sacrum to the shoulder.

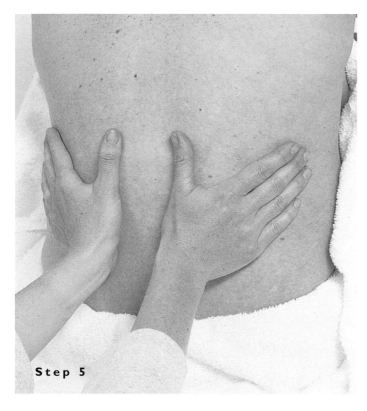

Step 5

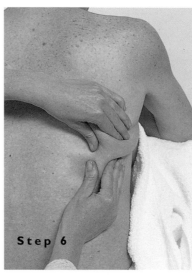

Step 8

5. Move your hands in the opposite direction by cupping around her hips and moving down to the gluteals. With both hands knead and squeeze the gluteals, like kneading dough. This will help relieve your partner's backache and relax the muscles around the area, which in turn helps the dilation of the cervix (neck of the womb).

8. Effleurage around the shoulders to release the tension. Complete this by stroking lightly with the fingertips right down to the gluteals.

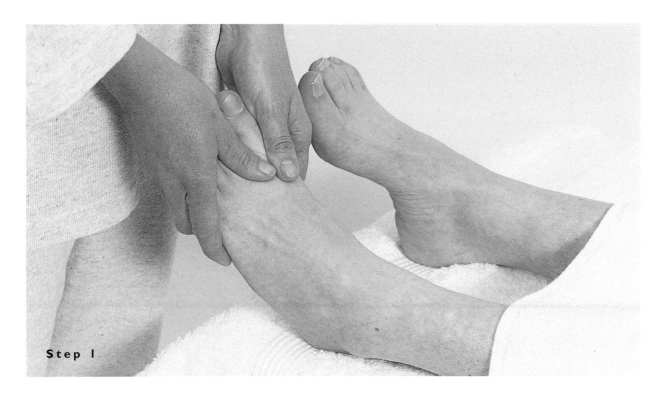

Step 1

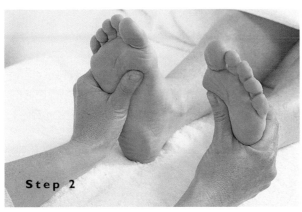

Step 2

Foot massage

Your partner should sit on a comfortable chair or lie on the floor with her back fully supported. You will be facing her and should sit on a stool or kneel at the side. During labor, it is best to massage both legs at once. Enlist a support person to massage the other leg.

1. Apply the oil of your choice to the feet and legs. While supporting the foot, massage the sole of the foot with your thumbs.

2. With your thumb, make tiny deep circles along the sole of the foot to the big toe. Hold the big toe and lean back to give it a stretch. Repeat these movements along the sole of the foot, moving to each toe in turn. Remember to traction each toe just by holding it and leaning back.

3. Massage the heel in circles, gradually working along the foot in circles to the ankles. Clasp your hands on either side of the leg and with firm upward pressure, glide up to the knee. Trace the knee with your fingers.

4. Gently bend the knee and glide your hands around the thigh using effleurage. Cupping the thigh between your hands pump firmly upwards.

5. Complete the massage by lightly stroking from the thigh to the toes and back again. Repeat, stopping at the toes.

6. Place the palms of your hands across the arch of your partner's feet to rebalance the energy field; this will work on the aura and the meridians. If your partner is mobile, remove any excess oil from the soles of her feet — this will help avoid risk of a fall.

While these are the suggested movements, the baby's processes may alter the whole procedure. Sequence is not important. Successful birth with a minimum of stress is the aim of massage at this time.

Postnatal Massage

*Emotionally and physically balanced parents have time and energy
to take care of their baby. Massage helps the new mother release any stress and tension
that may have built up during the pregnancy and birth.*

assage after childbirth is enormously beneficial for the new mother. After a woman has given birth, she may experience emotional ups and downs caused by hormonal changes. These may vary from a momentary bout of "baby blues" to more serious feelings. There are many pressures, and the demands of a new baby and the accompanying workload may be excessive. This situation can cause anxieties, depression and a feeling of isolation.

Take time to pamper yourself. Acknowledge that you are more important than the seemingly endless tasks. If the parents' needs are neglected, they will not be able to cope with their baby's needs. Emotionally and physically balanced parents have time and energy to take care of their baby.

Massage helps the mother release any stress and tension that may have built up during the pregnancy. Aromatherapy can play an important part after childbirth too. The essential oils not only have antibiotic, antiseptic, and antibacterial properties, but they are emotionally and spiritually uplifting. See the chapter on aromatherapy for more information.

The following instructions are addressed to the massage giver.

Face

Prepare a face oil of your partner's choice, but if she is breast feeding remember that some essential oils may affect the production of milk. The dilution is 5 drops of essential oil in 1 oz (30 ml) of base carrier oil. Jojoba is a delightful base oil, but a little may be added to sweet almond, extra virgin olive oil or grapeseed oil to reduce the cost. Again, do not exceed the dilution ratio of essential oil to base carrier oil. Since so small a quantity is required you may be able to afford one of the more expensive essential oils. Neroli, rose,

chamomile or lavender would all be suitable for a face massage. Stand behind your partner and using upward strokes, apply the oil up the neck and the face.

1. Using your palms, stroke your partner's forehead with alternating hands. Make the action smooth and continuous.

2. Gently squeeze along her eyebrows with your first finger and thumb, sliding off onto the temple.

3. With the pads of your thumbs, which are pointing towards each other across the forehead just above the eyebrow ridge, press and slide repeatedly until you reach the temple area. Here, lightly direct the tips of your thumbs into the area to assist drainage of the lymphatic vessels. Never use pressure in this sensitive spot. Continue working up the forehead to the hairline in the manner described.

4. With only the lightest touch of your fingertips, slide around the eye socket. Ensure that no oil gets into your partner's eyes at any time and that you do not stretch the delicate skin here.

5. Massage either side of the nose with circular movements, then continue along the cheekbones to the temples to encourage sinus drainage.

6. Gently pinch around the ears and pull the ear lobes.

7. Slide your fingers down to the center of the jaw and in small circles move out to the end of the jawbone. This will help to tone the muscles and to drain the lymphatic vessels.

8. Finish with upward strokes on the neck.

*Ask your doctor or midwife
how soon after the birth you should
start having massages.*

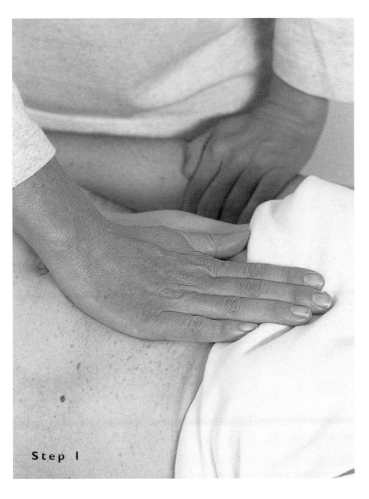

Step 1

Abdominal massage

Stand to the right of your partner. Apply the oil with the palm of your hand, working clockwise.

1. Place your right hand on your partner's solar plexus (the heel of your hand is placed just above the navel, with the fingers pointing up under the rib cage) while the palm of your left hand is held over the inside of your partner's right elbow. This position allows polarity flow, which is the movement of electrical energy through the body. In Western terms, it is positive and negative, in Eastern thought it is an aspect of yin and yang.

2. Place the points of your thumbs on the lower edge of the breastbone (sternum), now run them outwards under the rib cage, so that your fingers slide under the waist until the fingertips touch. Make sure your left foot is forward in a lunge position, with your right foot well back. Keeping your back straight to avoid strain, lean back as you lift your partner slightly while stretching along the top of her hips. To drain the lymph fluids, direct the fingertips down to the groin pressing softly through the abdominal tissues. Repeat this movement several times.

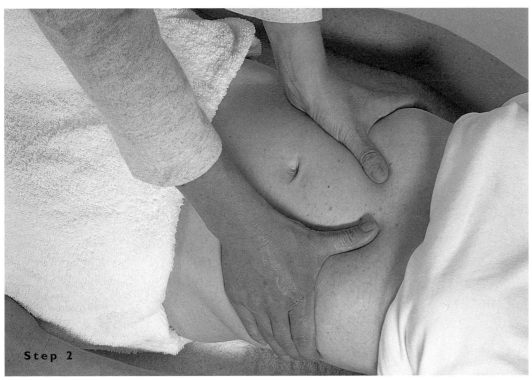

Step 2

In many countries where traditional practices are followed, it is the custom to massage the new mother regularly for six weeks after she gives birth. It is usually a female relative who gives the massage.

Arms

Hand and arm massage is an excellent way to ease tired muscles. Apply oil with smooth effleurage strokes sliding up the arm and returning to the hand.

1. Hold your partner's left hand while doing wringing, sliding squeezes in a kneading action up her arm. Use your finger pads to circle the elbow. Continue to the shoulder. Slide back down the arm and place a cushion under her elbow.

2. Work around the wrist with your thumbs then slide onto the palm. Mobilize the carpals (finger bones) by moving them up and down with both your hands. Stroke along each finger, then gripping each lightly, lean back to traction it.

3. Complete this section with light fingertip stroking down the arm and off the fingers.

4. Repeat the massage on the right arm.

Hand and arm massage is an excellent way to ease tired muscles. Apply oil with smooth effleurage strokes sliding up the arm and returning to the hand.

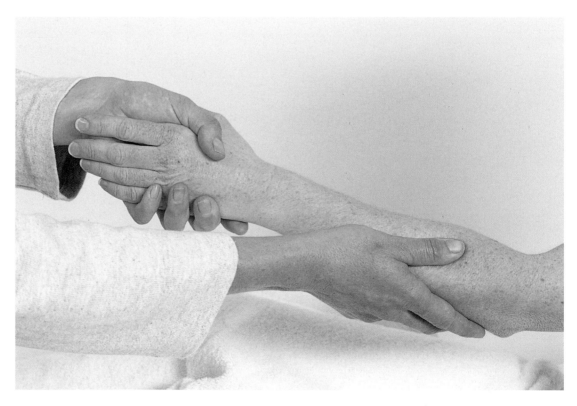

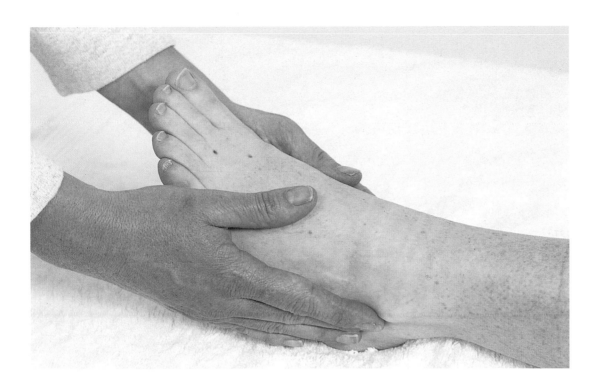

Ankles

After the birth some women will find that they have edema (fluid retention) of the ankles. Bathing in warm water (not hot) and gentle massage will help. Wrap the hand around the foot and stroke upwards. From the ankle upwards wrap both hands around the leg and move smoothly upwards. Use 2 drops each of geranium and cypress oils for the bathing. Frequent rests with the legs elevated will help overcome this condition.

General

Breast care

Breast massaging is very soothing during the first few days after delivery. To stimulate lactation use 10 drops of sweet fennel oil to ¾ oz (20 mls) of sweet almond oil. Massage the breasts with the palms in a circular movement.

Start under the arm and follow the breast around and up between the cleavage. Do not get any oil on the nipples. Massage the breasts after a feed. Make sure the massage oil is completely washed away before feeding the baby. This massage may be done twice a day.

For engorgement, chamomile and lavender compresses will help. Fill a small bowl with cool water and add a few drops of the essential oil; agitate well to disperse the oil. Place a cotton cloth, washcloth or small towel on top of the water, squeeze out and apply to the breasts after the baby has been fed.

Back massage

After the strain of pregnancy, childbirth and the constant lifting of the baby, the woman's back will benefit from a massage. It will help to tone tired muscles and stretched ligaments. Use a relaxing essential oil such as lavender in a blend. Follow the sequence outlined earlier.

Perineal care

There can be damage to the perineal tissue during childbirth. Use a basin or a sitz (hip) bath prepared with 2 drops of lavender, marjoram, cypress or juniper. Agitate the water to disperse the essential oils. Such bathing will improve the skin and hasten the healing around the perineal region.

Baby Massage

*Because babies are curled up in the womb, massage helps
the baby "open" to the world by encouraging opening of hands, flexing of toes,
spontaneous kicking and arm waving.*

Once the baby is born and the umbilical cord is cut, this new small being exists in its own right, separate from its mother. The baby's growth is quite rapid in the early stages of life. After months of being restricted in the womb, massage will encourage the baby's limbs to stretch.

As each baby is individual, the massage sequences and techniques must be adapted not only to suit the baby, but also to allow for particular moods and times of day. Because babies are curled up in the womb, massage, as well as creating a bonding, sharing contact, helps your baby "open" to this new environment. A primary aim of baby massage is to encourage opening of the hands, flexing of the toes, spontaneous kicking and arm waving. The strokes of baby massage move down the body from the head and from the trunk outwards along the limbs. All pressures must be light. This procedure is the opposite to that used in general massage, which follows the return of fluids, avoiding pressure on lymphatic and venous valves by moving firmly up the limbs, back to the heart. In baby massage, strokes working away from the heart are executed lightly. Of course babies also have as many one way valves in their fluid systems as adults, so the pressures must never be so strong as to put the delicate valves in both the veins and the lymphatic vessels at risk. Thus, although the strokes in baby massage are concentrating on working down the body and limbs as outlined in the chapter on basic massage movements, most movements are either stroking or gentle squeezing. The squeezing is light and the fingers slide to the next squeeze, never exerting any force that would be damaging to the frail new blood vessels.

Instinctively, babies are born with only two fears — the fear of falling and the fear of loud noises. To overcome these fears, always place your baby in a secure position for the massage. If you are not comfortable massaging while seated on the floor, make sure your baby won't roll off the bed, table or chair. This is especially so once the baby can roll spontaneously, usually at about 11–14 weeks. Ensure you have everything you need before beginning the massage and take all possible precautions against sudden or loud noise so an atmosphere of peace will prevail.

For further information on preparation and the best time for massaging your baby, see page 12.

Having fully prepared for your baby's massage, you must decide what position will be most suitable for your baby. Your baby's sense of security is of first importance and that is only possible if the person performing the massage is in a comfortable, sustainable position. Kneeling, especially when sitting back on the heels, may be damaging to the medial knee ligaments. If starting in this position, you would be wise to change your position when you turn your baby over, before working on her back. To keep your own body in good condition, remember to bend from the hips when massaging, keeping your back straight. Bending from the waist and leaning forward is tiring, and may damage your back — especially if you twist sideways, to pick up a towel for example. *Simultaneous bending and twisting is a very common cause of back injury.* Basic care of your own posture is paramount if you are to stay well and so be able to care for your baby.

Roger Woodward, the internationally renowned pianist, when lecturing to senior music students, placed his hands on the piano keys and leaned forward, explaining that by using his whole body weight, he was able to gain a more controlled and delicate touch. The same rule applies to massage; by placing hands in the required position and leaning from the spine, effortless, precise control is achieved. This is better for the baby and also for the person massaging, as by using the body in this manner, strain on specific muscles is avoided.

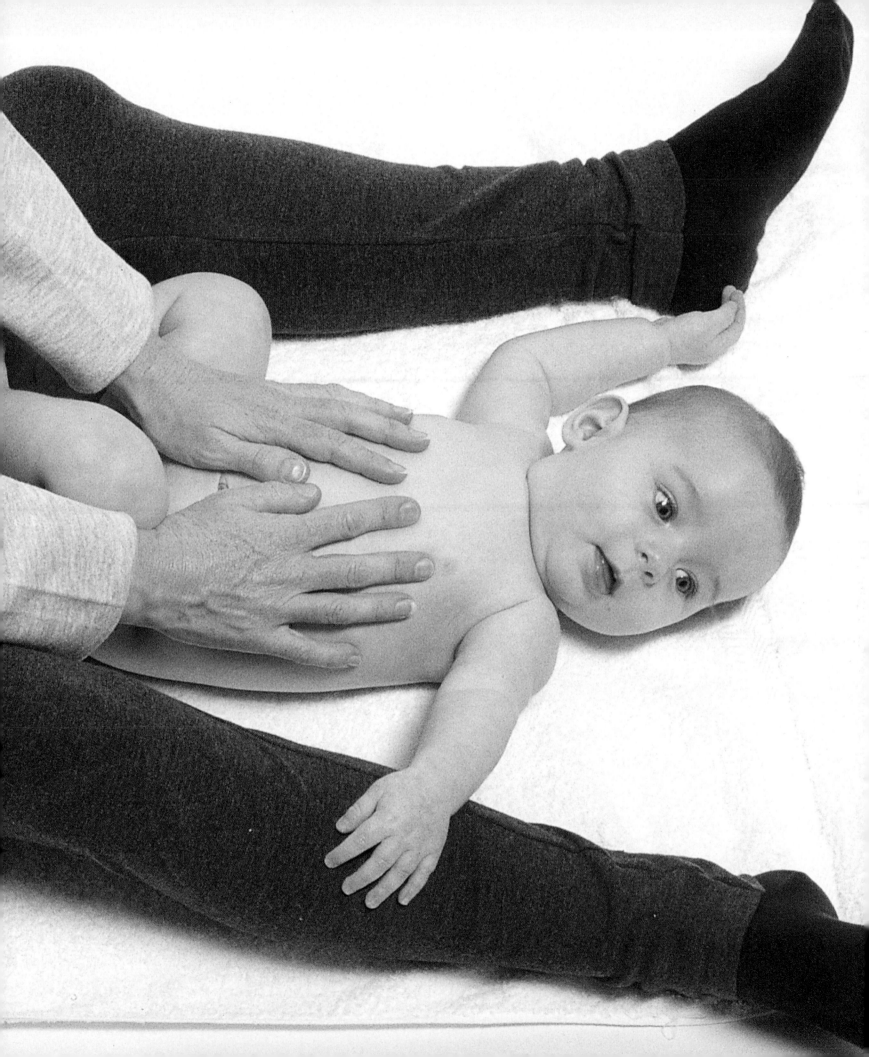

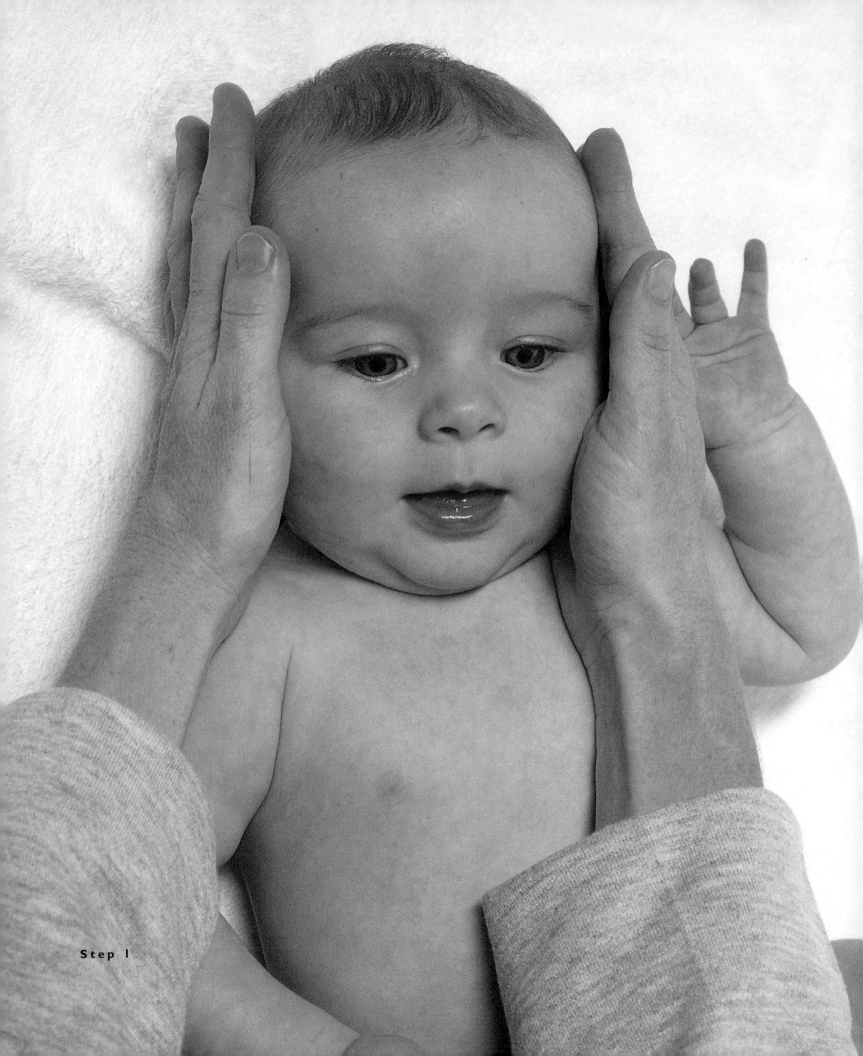

Step 1

Baby massage — a full body sequence

In general massage, the strokes are firm and move up the limbs
towards the heart. In baby massage, the strokes are light and gentle
and move down the body and limbs away from the heart.

The following sequence is appropriate for the massage of a healthy baby from a few months old onwards. The movements can also be adapted for the newborn, but always remember that a tiny baby needs more than anything else a caring, bonding touch.

Under six weeks of age, babies need only about ten minutes of massage, made up of stroking (sliding your hands on the skin of the face, abdomen and back) and gentle massage movements (gently moving the muscles beneath the skin on the gluteals, thighs, legs and arms). Do not use essential oils on the newborn.

A good time for a massage is after the baby's bath.

In each massage the left side is worked on first. This follows polarity and the oriental concept of one side being more receptive, while the other side is more outgoing.

Oils for baby massage

For baby massage use carrier oil only. Use essential oils only if required for an approved treatment for a specific problem. Once a baby is sitting up and moving easily, one drop of a gentle essential oil could be added to ⅔ oz (20 ml) massage oil. Take care with adding essential oils to the baby's bath. Once sitting, they will splash and put water into their mouths. It is much wiser to use diluted herbal teas such as chamomile in the bath.

After the baby is one year old, the dilution for 1 oz (30 ml) of massage oil is three drops of essential oil for the body. Do not use on the face until the child is 3 or 4 years old.

For all uses of essential oils on babies, apply the maxim "less is better then more".

Head

1. Gently hold your baby's face between your hands, while talking in a calm, quiet voice. Look into the baby's eyes while talking and, using both hands, stroke down either side of the face; this will achieve a feeling of encapsulation for you both.

2. Roll your hands sideways and slip them under the baby's head. Support the weight of the head on the heels of your hands while massaging the scalp with your fingertips moving in small circles. If your baby is a newborn, gently stroke the head in circles including the fontanells (soft spots).

3. Use your thumbs to stroke the ears. Press the ears with your thumb and forefinger, working from the top to the earlobe.

4. Finger stroke down the neck to the shoulders. Start with the little finger and use the tips of your four fingers in succession.

5. Turn your hands down to rest momentarily on the front of your baby's shoulders.

CAUTION

At all times hold your baby in such a way that the spine and neck are held safely. When babies are very young the weight of the head must be supported in all positions.

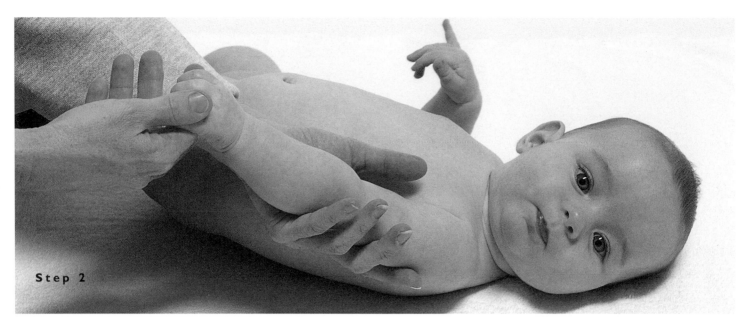

Step 2

Arms

1. If possible use both your hands and stroke from the baby's shoulders to the fingertips.

2. Move to the left arm. Using each hand alternately and starting at the shoulders squeeze and slide down the baby's arm to the fingers. Uncurl the fingers as you go.

3. If your baby's reaction is positive, repeat this movement, otherwise effleurage (stroke) the whole arm. The byword in massage is: "When in doubt, effleurage." It is always appropriate to use stroking movements in a massage.

The quality of any massage is improved by keeping contact with your child's body. Make all movements connected and flowing smoothly.

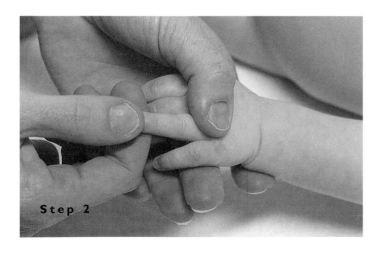

Step 2

Hands

1. Using small, circular movements massage the wrist with your thumb and forefinger. Open your baby's hand by stroking your thumb over the baby's palm. If your baby is not cooperative, present your index finger held sideways. Most babies will clutch at a finger presented like this, curling their fingers around it.

2. Play with your baby by moving the whole arm. Gradually open the hand and stroke each finger. Holding the hand with one of your hands, rotate and stretch each finger in turn, beginning with the little finger. To achieve a smooth action lightly hold one of the baby's fingers between your finger and thumb. Now lean backwards — use your body weight, not the muscles of your hands and arms.

The use of the whole body allows precise control that your baby will appreciate.

3. Repeating the above steps, progress across the hand, moving each finger.

4. Place your thumb sideways then close your baby's hand over your thumb. With your four fingers together, stroke up the back of the hand.

5. During each massage stay alert to what is happening under your hands. Complete the arm massage at the shoulders. Now move to the right arm and repeat.

Be sensitive to any sore spots. Feel for the freedom of swivelling in the joints of the wrist, elbow and shoulder. Do not exert pressure on the joints. Allow your baby freedom to move, to blend harmoniously with your movements. In this way each massage becomes an assessment and an awareness for you of your baby's development.

Chest

1. Stroke down the front of your baby's body from the shoulders to the toes in a general movement, using one or both hands depending on how they fit. If using one hand after the other, keep the movement continuous by leaving the first hand in place until the other takes over. In this way your baby will not be aware of the change from one hand to the other.

2. Using your fingertips, circle your baby's breast, avoiding the nipples. Be aware of the ribs as your fingers slide over the area. Use the very tip of your little fingers to lightly trace each rib, then slide them back along the space between the ribs, giving the muscles a very slight stretch. Finish this movement with the fingers close together at the base of the neck.

Body Strokes

1. From your baby's neck, stroke sideways along the shoulders, slightly stretching the muscles.

2. Circle the shoulders, then slide your fingers into the armpits and stroke around to the center of the body, following the rib cage. The intercostal muscles (between the ribs) are vital for breathing. The development of a smooth breathing action is of paramount importance for babies.

3. Stroke up and down your baby's body from the armpits to the thighs. Make this movement slow and smooth, or vigorous, depending on what reaction you wish to achieve. Finish the strokes with the hands positioned just below the ribs.

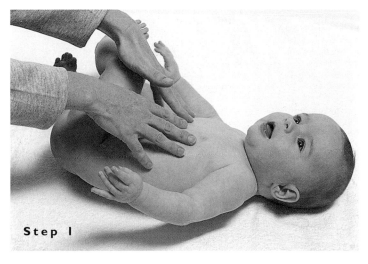

Step 1

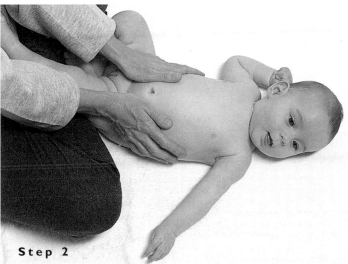

Step 2

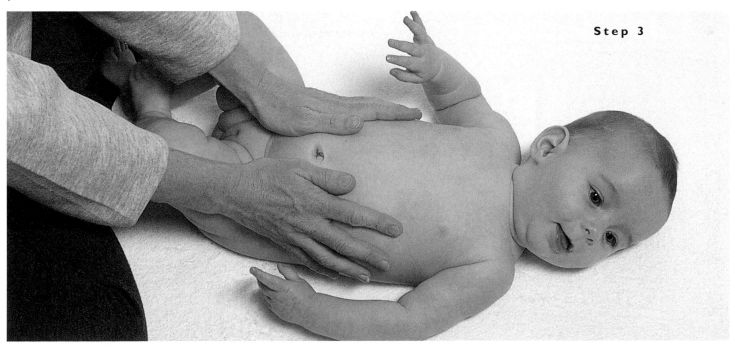

Step 3

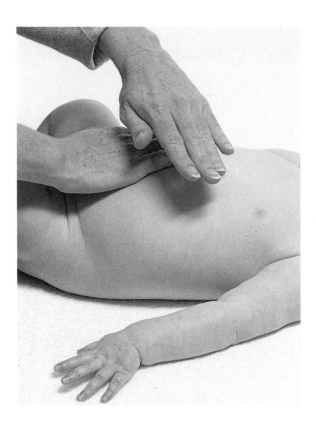

Abdomen

If your baby is a newborn, do not massage the abdomen if the umbilical cord is still in place. Once the area is healed, massage in a clockwise direction with your finger tips or the palm of your hand.

1. This movement is always done clockwise to follow the peristaltic action of the intestines. Keep your hand as flat as possible and soothe the stomach as you circle. At all times watch your baby's face while you work, but especially when working on the abdominal region. Note any negative reaction or any sore spot. Go very lightly over the lower abdomen, as this is where your baby's bladder is located. Pressure there is not only always uncomfortable, it is unwise.

2. Using the pads of your fingers circle the navel. Start with your left hand making circles around the baby's navel. Cross your right hand over the left and position your fingers to form an arc with the right hand. Thus the left hand keeps circling and, to prevent tying your arms in knots, the right hand makes arcs only at the appropriate place in the circles. Take care not to work too close to the navel and not to cause any distress to the baby.

3. Place your hands above and below your baby's navel and using your fingers circle it.

Some long strokes down the whole body, from shoulders to toes may be done now.

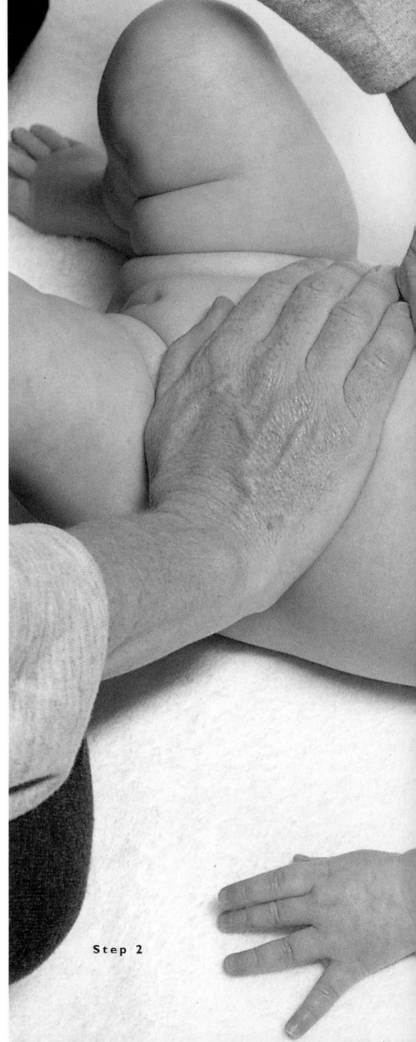

Step 2

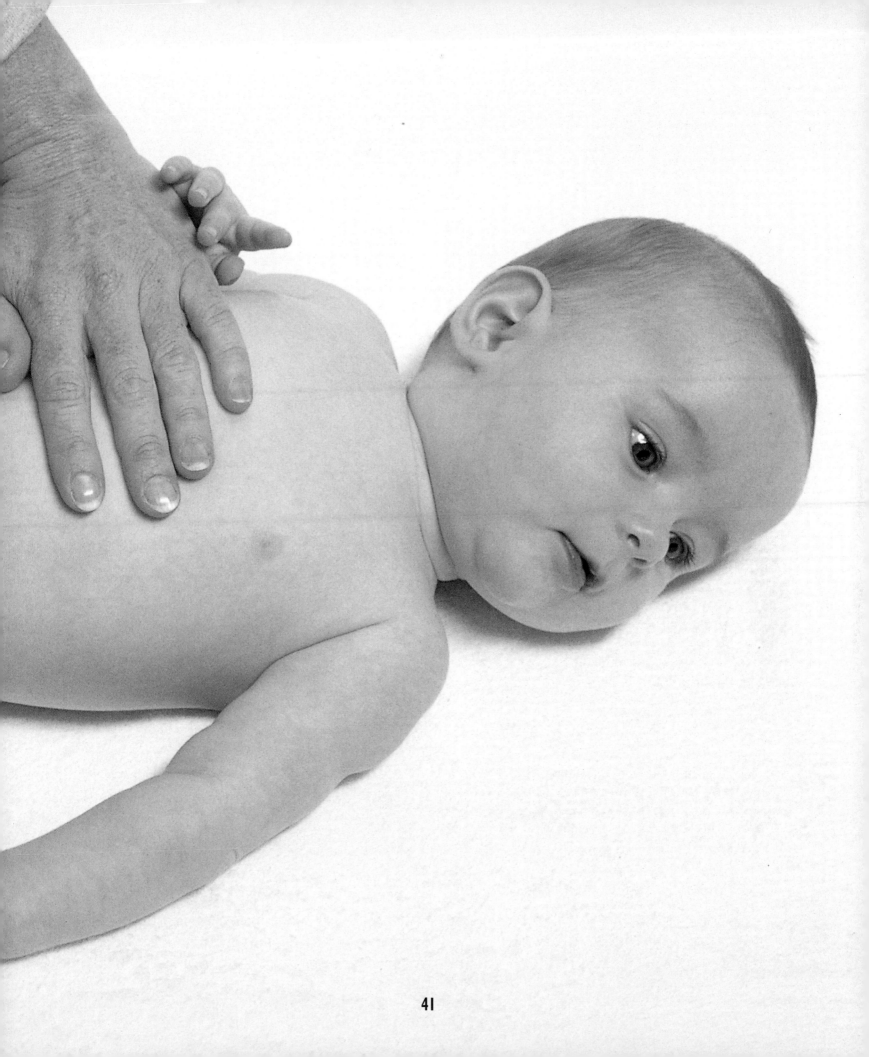

Step 2

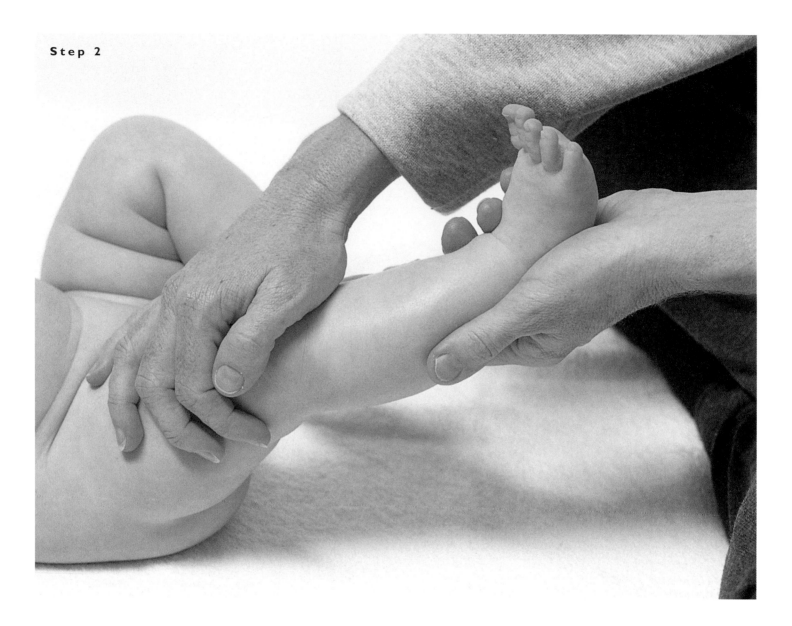

Legs

1. Effleurage (stroke) down the left leg, and run your hands smoothly and lightly back to the thigh.

   2. Squeeze along the leg to the foot. If suitable use both hands, otherwise hold the heel of the foot with one hand while squeezing and sliding along the leg with the other. Your baby might help by kicking during this stroke. The encouragement of coordinated free movement is one aim of baby massage, so do not restrain your baby's spontaneity. The experience should be pleasurable for you both.

   3. Follow with the massage of the left foot.

Take care not to cause discomfort in the baby's neck. Also, periodically, change the direction of your baby's face from side to side. Otherwise, only one position will become neurally imprinted in your baby's brain.

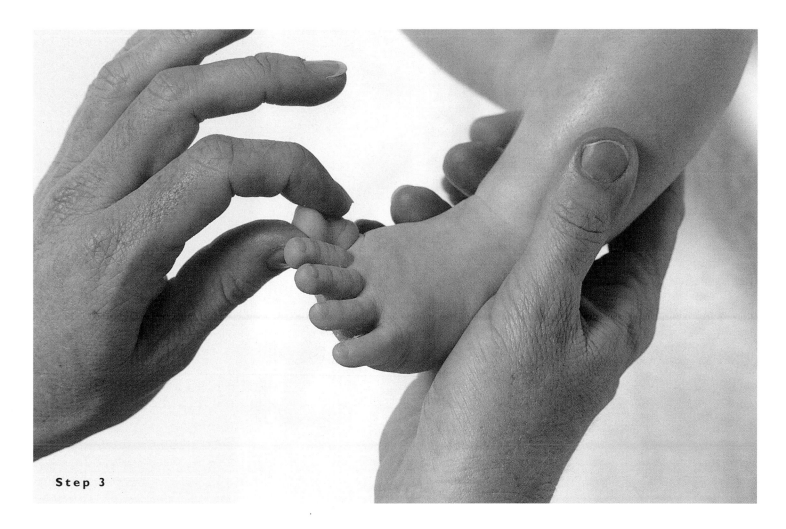

Step 3

Feet

1. With the pads of your fingers circle the ankles. Support the baby's left heel with one hand while you stroke down the sole of the foot with the thumb of your other hand. Place your hand with the fingers together over the top of the baby's foot and stroke the sole with the pad of your thumb.

Although the thumb pressure on the sole may be moderate, do not exert any pressure with the fingers since the nerves are close to the surface on top of the foot.

2. Begin at the inside (medial) edge and stroke in parallel lines from the heel to the toe. Finish at the side (lateral part) of the foot. Use your right hand on your baby's left foot, thus your thumb is drawn down the sole to the big toe. Keep the pressure firm and even. When each stroke reaches the toes quickly slide your thumb back to the heel to do the next stroke, then move across the foot as described. Although you lift your thumb to return to the heel each time, if the movement is smooth and quick the sensation to your baby will be one of continuity.

3. Beginning with the little toe lightly rotate and stretch each toe in turn. Control your movement with body weight as previously described. A traditional rhyme goes with this movement: "This little pig went to market, this little pig stayed at home..." and most babies seem to enjoy the rhythmic effect of the verse.

4. Repeat on the right leg and right foot.

AFTER completing the massage to the legs and feet, turn the baby over onto the tummy. If newborn, you may prefer to lie your baby across your thighs. If you have been kneeling, you may benefit from a change of position at this stage.

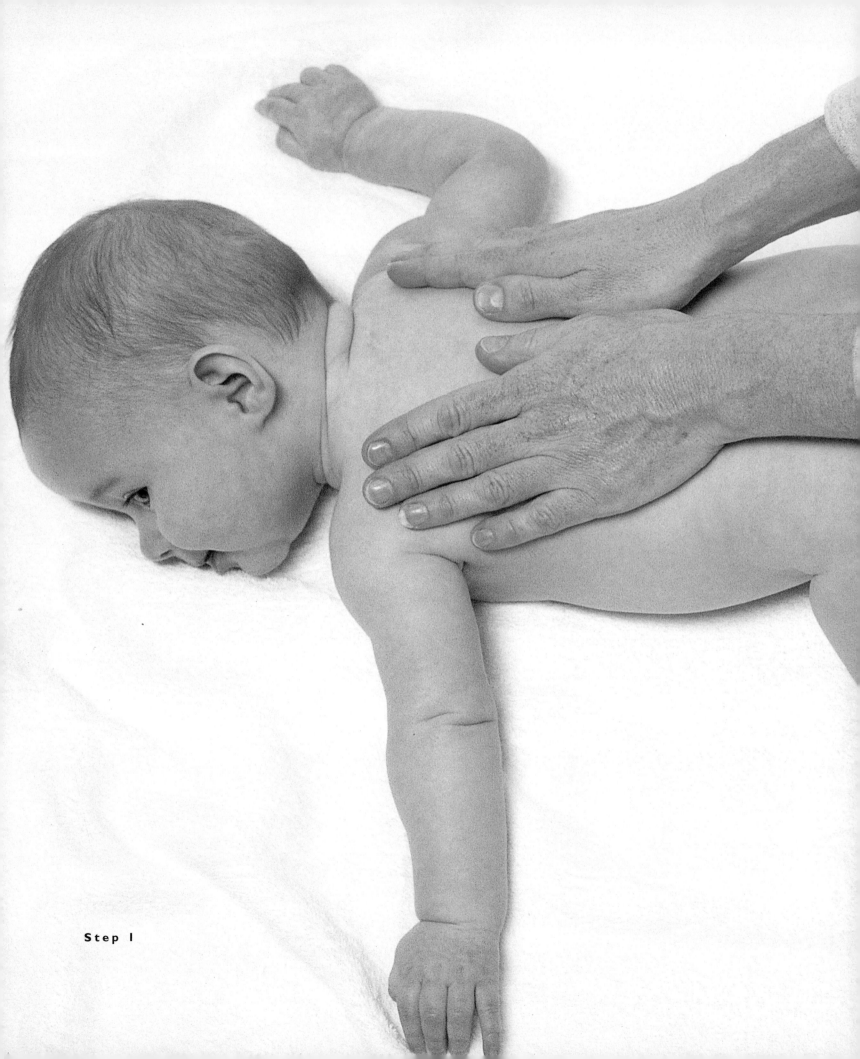

Step 1

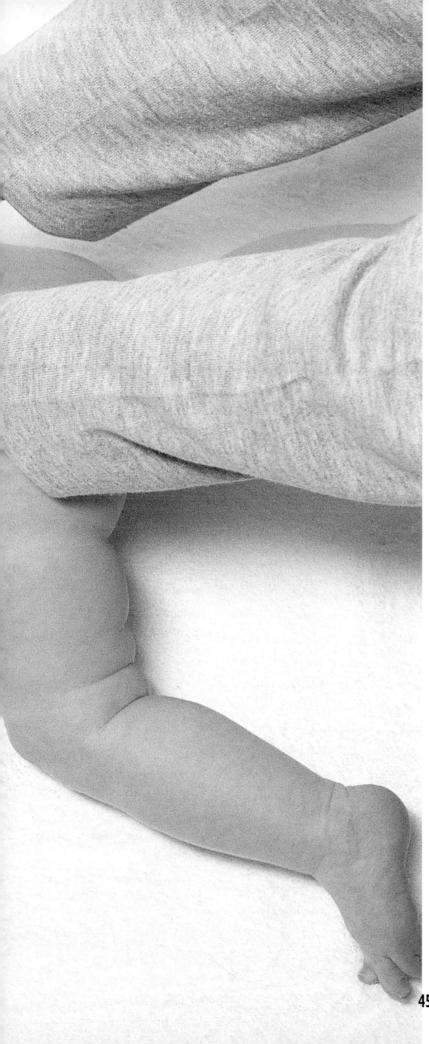

Back

1. Cupping both your hands around the baby's head, stroke to the shoulders and onto the back. Using both hands stroke up and down the baby's back. Keep your fingers together so your hand works as one unit from its heel to its fingertips. Concentrate on the energy flowing through your hands.

For the newborn, just slide your hands alternately moving from the neck to the gluteals. Repeat this very soothing movement several times.

2. Having effleuraged (stroked) up and down your baby's back using your whole hand, finish with a stroke at the buttocks. Keeping your thumbs either side of the spine, and having your fingers together around your baby's sides, slide up the back and down again several times, leading with your thumbs.

Be conscious of feeling the baby's vertebra between your thumbs. Never put any pressure on the spine and use your body weight not just your arm muscles to keep a light even flow to the whole process.

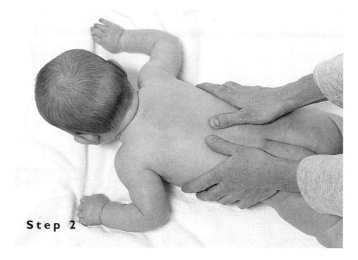

Step 2

Check your own posture. Keep your back straight, whatever position you are working in. Bend from the hips not the waist, and control the pressure with your body weight, not your muscles. This technique will produce a smoother action and give better control to the massage, allowing development of gentle precision.

45

Gluteals

1. Massage around the gluteals (buttocks). Be careful to avoid any chafing. Knead these major muscles by squeezing, stretching and releasing. This may need to be done with only fingers and thumbs. These muscles are the deepest in the body and are used extensively in most movements, even when we are seated. Avoid your baby's anus.

2. By using your first two fingers and thumbs, roll the flesh from the baby's thigh up to the sacrum (end of the spine). Make these rolls fan out from the base of the buttocks (gluteals) to the sides to the pelvis.

Stroke lightly down the body from head to toes to complete this part of the massage. Light stroking stimulates the nerve endings.

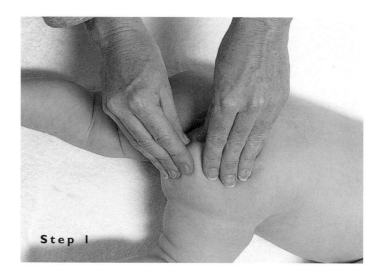

Step 1

The number of times you repeat any movement will be governed by your baby's reactions.

Face

1. Turn your baby back to face you and gently stroke across the forehead, using the pads of your thumbs. Avoid the baby's eyes, and be careful not to let any oil get into them, nor near them.

2. Stroke the nose and around the mouth then stroke the cheeks and along the jawbone.

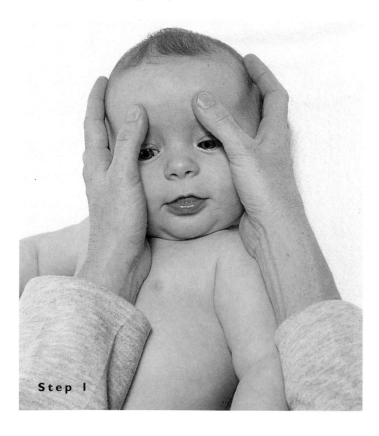

Step 1

To complete the massage do some final full length strokes right down the body from head to toe.

Finish with a kiss and a cuddle.

Babies with special needs

As with all babies, loving touch and massage will give babies with disabilities confidence. Their sense of self will be positive and strong, a confidence that will stay with them throughout life.

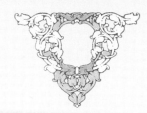

The skin protects us by keeping our bodies intact. It regulates our temperature through fluid release and also protects us from many harmful agents, partly by the slightly acid PH value in its mantle. Skin also contains the nerves that control our reactions to pressure, heat, cold and pain. Skin is a sensory organ that registers emotions.

Children who are never or rarely touched are seriously deprived. Much of the damage done to these children can be reversed with loving, gentle touching, the kind of touching that is of the utmost importance for any child who is to grow with an innate sense of security.

Disabilities

There are specialized facilities available to assist parents cater for their children who have special needs. For details of what is available in your area, contact your local hospital, government authority or community center.

Blind or deaf

As with all babies, loving touch and massage will give babies with disabilities confidence. Their sense of self will be positive and strong. The more they are touched, the more aware they become of their body shape. As their sense of touch is heightened, the keener their sense of the outside world will be. Allow your baby lots of skin contact. For example, touch the bare legs or put the child to your breast.

Use your whole hand as much as possible, concentrating on your energy flow. For the blind baby, who usually has an increased sensitivity to touch, arrange a variety of textures so the baby's tactile sense will keep developing.

As deaf babies grow, be tolerant of the noises they may make, as they are unaware of, and therefore unable to control, the volume of sounds they create.

Paralysis

Children who are paralysed need constant stimulation to encourage a neural response. Begin by massaging (effleurage) any unaffected part of the body. This (remote) stimulation is known to be beneficial to a damaged nervous system. Follow the effleurage of the area by using feather light finger stroking. Such stroking of the nerve endings strengthens response along the nerve pathways. Improvement of the fluid circulations is also an important aspect of massaging for the affected area. Work under the guidance of a qualified practitioner and carry out their suggested movements. Of particular benefit, the holding of stretches of muscles in the restricted areas, beyond the usual timing, may help restore the desired muscle performance.

Downs Syndrome

There have been some remarkable developments shown in Downs Syndrome children who have been constantly and expertly massaged from their earliest months. Contact your nearest Downs Syndrome association for further details.

Massage for Common Troubles

The benefits of your baby's massage can be heightened by the use of herbs and essential oils. For example, use the essential oil of chamomile in a vaporizer or room spray to help calm your baby.

Colic

Often parents think their baby is smiling when colic is causing a grimace. Colic is pain caused by contractions of the intestines and can be distressful for babies.

1. Prepare a chamomile tea in water that is just slightly warmer than usual for a baby's bath. Lie your baby face up on your hand. While gliding your baby through the bath water, massage the abdomen in a clockwise direction with your other hand.

2. When too big for this technique, the baby can be seated at the end of a baby bath. Massage the abdomen as shown.

3. Whenever possible support the massaging with the use of herbs. For example, give your baby warm chamomile tea in a bottle and use the essential oil in a burner or room spray. These additional ideas will enhance the massage.

4. Any fruits high in acid, like pineapple, or over indulgences of most sorts, may cause colic in a breast-fed baby.

Crying

Crying is most often caused by:

- tiredness
- hunger or thirst
- soiled diapers
- uncomfortable surfaces in the baby's bed
- pain due to medical problems

As you get to know your baby you will be able to distinguish the various causes of crying by the tone and intensity of the crying. Unless the crying is due to a serious problem or medical condition for which you will take appropriate action, holding the baby and massaging as suggested is pacifying for minor causes of distress.

Hold your baby across your chest and repeatedly stroke from the head down to the feet. Combine these strokes with peaceful rocking.

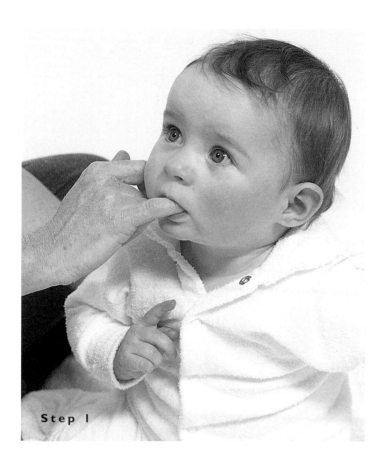

Step 1

Teething

When the teeth are ready to come through, the gums will be red and swollen and sore to touch. Giving your baby a rusk or other teething device will assist the teeth and give some relief to the baby. You can also buy a suitable commercial ointment to massage into the gums.

Remember that essential oils should never be used internally, and are not to be used directly on babies.

1. Taking care not to damage the delicate mucous membranes in the baby's mouth, use a finger dipped in iced water to work the ointment into the inflamed gums. If there is no ointment available, the cooling action of a cold finger or teething device will be almost as effective. As more teeth come, beware of the bite.

2. At teething time you can also use general massage strokes that you know are soothing to your baby. Stroke your baby's face or give a general body massage.

Note: At teething time some babies develop diaper rash. Because they tend to dribble more while teething, they lose more fluid than usual, making the urine more concentrated. The increased ammonia in the urine causes skin irritation.

Constipation

This is more common with bottle fed babies than those receiving breast milk, although breast fed babies also may suffer constipation at times. The abdomen massage increases the blood flow, which in turn improves the peristaltic action. Ensure an increased fluid intake to assist in overcoming this problem.

Rotate the palm of your hand clockwise in a smooth continuous movement. Having slightly warmed a teaspoon (5 ml) of sweet almond oil, add one drop of lavender to it and rub it in well. This circling will soothe the abdomen and encourage the movement of the bowel.

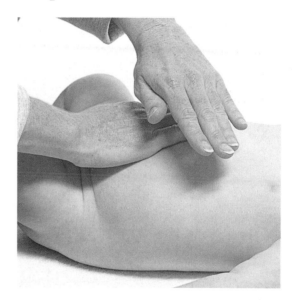

To ease constipation, you can also massage the abdomen while the baby is in the bath.

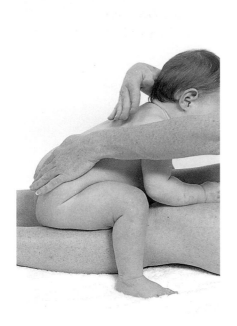 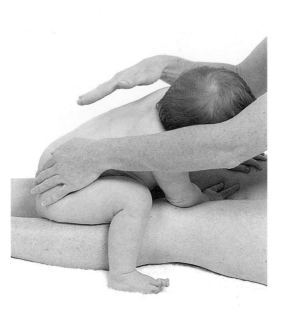 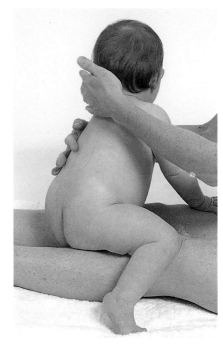

Lethargy

Although massage usually "soothes", stimulating massage will benefit all systems, generating energy and enlivening the lethargic baby. Use a light touch at the beginning, then increase the pressure slightly and move quickly to stimulate the circulation and the neural response. Seek medical advice if the baby is always slow and lethargic.

Burn tangerine oil to improve the atmosphere and play sounds your baby enjoys. Avoid interruptions or distractions.

Irritability

The back is the area with the greatest number of accessible nerves, so begin by pressing with your fingertips down either side of the baby's spine, from the neck to the tail bone. Alternatively, work with the baby lying on the back.

Talk quietly, or repeat a rhyme, while squeezing along the shoulders and down the body. Hold the baby's body closely between your hands as you move down the trunk. When you reach the feet squeeze and play with them.

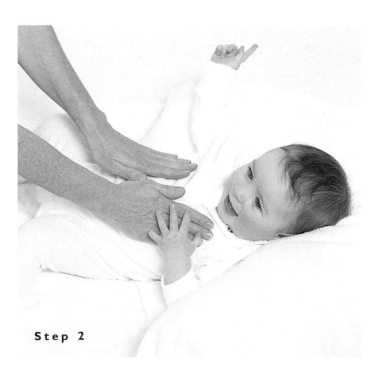

Step 2

As undressing may cause the irritable baby to become more unsettled, leave the clothes on.

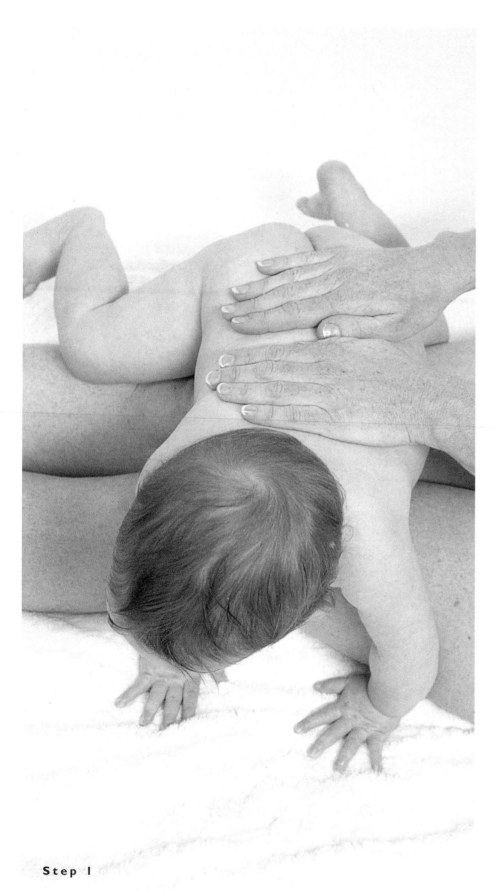

Step 1

Poor weight gain

1. Lie your baby face downwards across your legs close to your body. Keep both your hands close together so you cover the maximum area with each stroke and effleurage the baby's back and legs. Stroke the feet and squeeze them.

2. Turn your baby and again using both hands effleurage the baby's front.

3. For extra skin nourishment, add one drop of tangerine oil to a teaspoon of olive oil. Diffuse the air with a drop each of bergamot and orange essential oils in a vaporizer or bowl of hot water.

Dry skin

Add one drop of rose, roman chamomile or lavender oil to 1 oz (30 ml) sweet almond oil or jojoba oil and apply a little to the baby's skin by stroking on gently after bathing or changing. Note that except for overdue babies it is unusual for babies' skin to be dry.

If the baby is under six months old or not developing well, use the carrier oil only.

Premature babies

While in a humidicrib, the premature baby is the focus of attention. Attached to electronic equipment, the baby is given constant care by the specialist nursing staff and parents. When strong enough to go home the baby will at first miss the movements of the hospital. The closeness of the mother's touch is vital in establishing bonding and normal growth patterns.

While supporting your baby in a way that enables skin to skin contact, stroke all over the baby's back and front. Cup your hands to give your baby a "held" feeling. Hold the head between both your hands. Let your baby lean on you while you gently squeeze the hands and feet.

Chafing and rashes

One drop of calendula oil may be added to 1oz (30 ml) sweet almond oil. Gently pat a small quantity of this mixture into the affected area.

An unguent made from 1 teaspoon (5 ml) melted beeswax, 2 teaspoons (10 ml) sweet almond oil, to which one drop of the calendula oil is added, can be used as a barrier cream on the skin as it will keep the skin drier and hold the calendula oil longer.

For an alternative add 1 drop of lavender oil to 1 oz (30 ml) sweet almond or jojoba oil. Use half a teaspoon and apply gently to the baby's bottom.

If the rash persists this is one place where mineral baby oil is suitable as it is a barrier to urine if the baby cannot be changed constantly.

Otherwise talk to your pharmacist to recommend a suitable cream. One drop of myrrh or roman chamomile or benzoin mixed into the cream and patted onto the rash will soothe and help to heal the skin. Just pat, never rub a sore area.

As a treatment for diaper rash, calendula petals may be added to a small bowl of warm water. Place your baby into the bowl for a few minutes after every diaper change. Alternatively, one drop of sandalwood oil or myrrh oil could be added to the water. Swish the water around to disperse the oil before bathing the baby.

Take care to ensure the baby does not splash this water in the eyes.

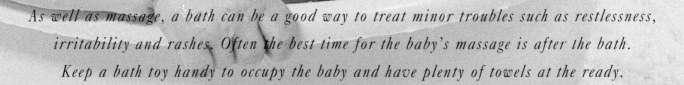

As well as massage, a bath can be a good way to treat minor troubles such as restlessness, irritability and rashes. Often the best time for the baby's massage is after the bath. Keep a bath toy handy to occupy the baby and have plenty of towels at the ready.

Colds

Leave your baby clothed. Place a bowl of hot water nearby but out of the baby's reach. Add one drop each of lemon, sandalwood and eucalyptus essential oils to the water. Hold your baby against you and rub the baby's back while the prepared oil diffuses nearby. Avoid subjecting your baby to sudden temperature changes while the cold is evident.

Try to breathe in the same rhythm as your baby, which will be faster than your normal rate. When you and your baby are synchronized with each other, slow your breathing a little to help your baby copy you and use the lungs more efficiently.

Shallow breathing

Place your hand on your child's rib cage, with a firm but not heavy pressure. Now stroke elsewhere using your other hand. This stroking is to divert attention, while the hand held over the lungs will remind your baby's brain that there is no movement under your hand and that the chest cavity (thoracic) can expand more fully. After a short while the breathing will become deeper and more even. Strengthening neural pathways in this fashion will improve the baby's respiratory system. Take a moment to carry out this procedure each time you massage your baby.

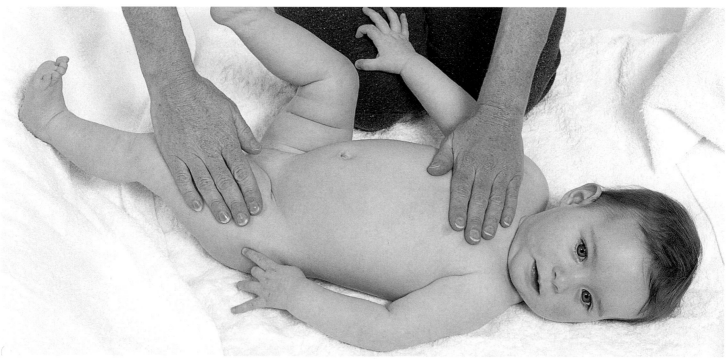

Massage for Children

As children progress from the baby stage, they will continue to enjoy the attention of a massage. Now the massage strokes are applied firmly up *the arms and legs, followed with a light touch* down *the limbs.*

No human will thrive without human touch. This especially applies to children who are insecure, for whatever reason. Adopted children are bonded more successfully if they are given loving massages. Not only is the touch of such value, but all children enjoy being the focus of attention, which is the case when they are being massaged.

Through massage, parents can produce positive reactions from their children. This will strengthen the parent-child bond, enabling the parents to experience the happiness their children bring.

The purpose of early baby massage is to help the infant move freely after the constriction of the womb, but as the child grows the principles of fluid flow in the body need to be applied. Now the child is older, the strokes should be applied firmly *up* the limbs, but only very light touch is used when coming back *down* the arms and legs. This mode of massage can be gradually adapted for a healthy baby from about five months onwards. As children grow, they will exert their wishes about when, how and where, and even why, they want a massage. The decisions taken should be mutually pleasing. Above all, the massage must be fun, giving joy to both participants, whatever their ages.

If the child becomes restless, keep the massage short. Experiment with the following suggestions to find out what your child prefers. For information about oils to use for a children's massage see the chapter on aromatherapy.

If you wish to use essential oils for children's massage, prepare ⅔ oz (20 ml) base carrier oil with 3–5 drops essential oil.

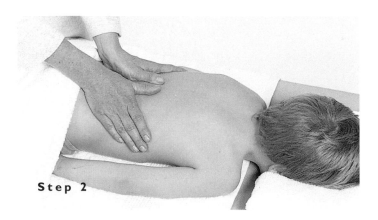

Step 2

Back

1. Begin at the sacrum. Using effleurage (a gentle smoothly flowing stroke) move up the child's back, your hands either side of the spine. Lead with the fingers first, then next with the thumbs. Stroke up to the neck then back down the sides of the child's back.

2. Using the movement of frictions (small circular movements made with the pads of the thumbs or fingers) begin at the sacrum, then work up the muscles on either side of the spine.

3. Use the tips of your fingers to tap the muscles to stimulate the child's whole back.

4. Finish with a very light effleurage as in step 1.

There is no need to remove the child's clothes if the child prefers to keep them on. A massage through light clothes can be just as effective.

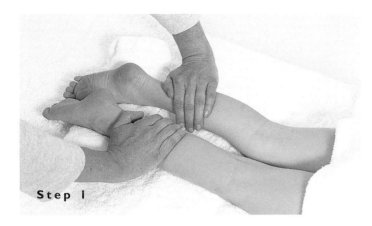

Step 1

Legs and feet

1. Using one hand on each leg, begin at the child's feet and massage up the legs. On the calves and thighs, work firmly with a "push, pull" kneading action.

2. Slide lightly back to the feet.

3. Rotate the ankle and using your body weight pull the toes as described on page 18.

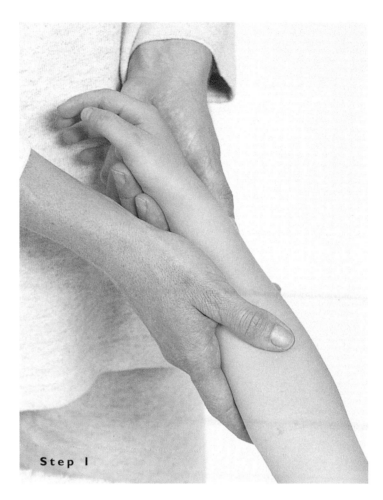

Step 1

Abdomen

When massaging the abdomen, always use clockwise movements.

Gently oil the abdomen, always moving in a clockwise direction. Begin with the left hand moving in a complete circle. Keep the left hand circling. Place the right hand on the abdomen to trace a partial circle as the left hand goes past.

Use your fingers to move up, across and down the colon. The colon (large intestine) runs up the right side, across the abdomen, and down the left side of the body in an inverted "U".

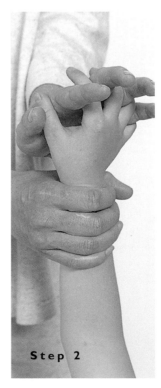

Step 2

Arms and hands

1. Effleurage (stroke) firmly from the fingertips to the shoulder of the child's left arm, returning lightly. Place your hands one on either side of the child's arm with your palms facing each other. Press inwards. With a gentle but sustained pressure, move your hands in circles up the arm from the wrist to the shoulder. Follow with strokes (effleurage) to the arm and hand.

2. Stretch and rotate the child's wrist.

3. Repeat the sequence on the right arm and hand.

Children Giving a Massage

If they have been massaged as babies and are used to it, children usually love to give a massage. They particularly enjoy the percussive "thumping" movements, and kneading and stroking are easy for a child's little hands.

f you have massaged your child through pregnancy, birth and "baby days", the desire to join in massaging will probably come spontaneously to that child. It will be fun for your child to be able to massage an adult. At the same time it is a good conditioning exercise for the child's left/right brain development.

Besides the physiological benefits, when a child gives a massage, the caring and sharing aspects of massage will help the child develop an empathy for other people, concern for their well-being and a generosity of spirit — essential qualities for later life.

Humans need human physical contact. A child's sense of self and self-esteem partly comes from how much they are touched in early childhood. Children need to feel loved and lovable, and appropriate touching is an affirmation of your love and their own appealing nature. Children who grow within the security of a loving and approving environment will expect – and receive – the same approval from others throughout their adult lives. As technology distances human contact in our modern world, frequent appropriate touching can be a counter to the often dehumanizing aspects of our increasingly technological society.

What follows are suggested skills, which can be practiced in any order. The most important thing is to have fun with your child and enjoy the time together.

After a hard day, the light touch of your child's hands on your forehead can help release tension and dissipate fatigue.

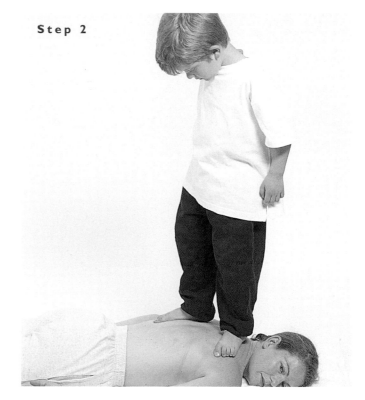

Back

1. Lie down in a comfortable "prone" position. The child can begin by stroking oil over your back, then rubbing with both hands up the middle and down the sides of your back.

2. If the child is light, and there are no problems with your back, he could walk up and down the back, placing the feet on either side of the spine. Make sure your child avoids the area between your ribs and hip bones, as damage may be done to your kidneys. The child can knead your tight muscles by wiggling and digging in his toes. Getting your child to walk on your back can be a great way to relieve tightness. In addition, the child will enjoy "walking all over you". Tell the child to avoid walking on the spine itself or on the kidney area between your ribs and hip bones.

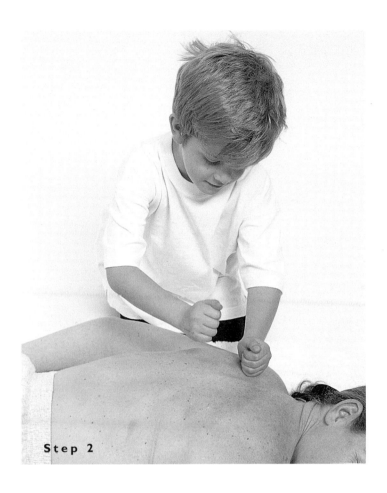

Step 2

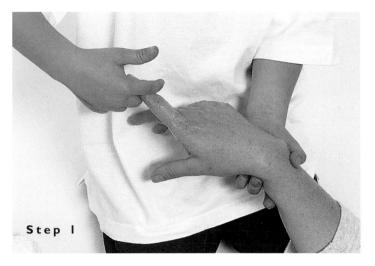

Step 1

Hands

1. Get the child to hold your hands and stroke and pull your fingers. Let the child be imaginative — this can be "like milking a cow". Pulling the fingers restores flexibility.

2. Get the child to rub your palm and the back of your hand. The child can rotate your wrist and stretch your hand both forward and backwards. Repeat on the other hand.

Shoulders

1. With closed fists, the child can rub the knuckles along your shoulders and down either side of your spine.

2. Keeping the hands closed, the child can use the knuckles in a percussive stroke — children enjoy being able to "thump" an adult.

3. To soothe your shoulders, the child can use the whole forearm. In this movement the child rubs the shoulder muscles, dodging the bones.

Step 2

The caring and sharing aspects of massage encourage a child's empathy for other people. This in turn develops qualities of consideration for others and generosity of spirit.

Face

Remind the child to avoid getting any oil in your eyes.

1. First, get the child to stroke your forehead, working outwards from the middle of the brow.

2. Then the child can stroke upwards from the chin to the hairline, again avoiding the eyes.

3. The child can finish with a tap of the fingertips along your jaw and up to the eyes. This will help to stimulate the circulation.

Aromatherapy
Using Essential Oils

Touch and smell are both senses we often take for granted. Essential oils penetrate the skin quickly to reach the bloodstream and are therefore a wonderful accessory to massage.

The pleasure of using the pure essences of fragrant plants has been recognized for centuries. Essential oils are pure concentrated extracts from selected plants. They are revered both for their fragrance and their therapeutic value. It is the use of these essential oils — in massage oils, room vaporizers and baths and so on — that is known as the practice of aromatherapy.

Many essential oils are naturally antibiotic, antiseptic, antibacterial and antifungal and are safe for both mother and baby if they are used in an appropriate manner.

Quality of essential oils

Unfortunately, as the renewed appreciation of essential oils and aromatherapy has grown in recent years, so too has the preponderance of merchandise of an inferior quality. Seek out a source of high quality oils. Price is often an indicator. If you see a range of oils offered all at the same price, beware. Those oils will be synthetic, and while they may smell the same as genuine essential oils, their properties are not known to be reliable and they will not have the same therapeutic values.

Genuine essential oils cannot all be the same price, because different plants offer varying yields of oil. Enormous quantities of tiny flowers are required to produce a sufficient amount of chamomile oil or rose oil for example, while the amount of oil produced from the leaves of the rosemary bush is more generous. *"Fragrant oil" is not essential oil — make sure you read the labels carefully.*

CAUTION
Essential oils must never be taken orally and should not be applied in undiluted form to the skin. Always mix them with a base carrier oil.

Storage of essential oils

Oils react to sunlight, therefore they should be stored in amber or dark bottles in a cool, dark place. The bottles need to have tightly fitting lids with dripolators to dispense the required drops. If your essential oil bottles do not have a fitted dripolator use an eye dropper. Keep one dropper for each oil. Oils are volatile and highly flammable, so treat them with care.

Base carrier oils

Use good quality base carrier oils such as sweet almond, grapeseed or extra virgin olive oil, with added jojoba, apricot, evening primrose, wheatgerm or vitamin E oil (tocopherol acetate) to make up 10% of the total blend. To 1 oz (30 ml) of base carrier oil add the number of drops of essential oil which are recommended depending on whether the massage blend is for use during pregnancy, childbirth, the postnatal period, or for use on a baby or child.

Massage blends

For a general adult massage, the usual ratio of essential oil to base oil is 10–15 drops of essential oil to 1 oz (30 ml) of base carrier oil. For facial massage, reduce the drops to 5 for each 1 oz (30 ml) carrier oil. For massage during pregnancy, add 2–5 drops of one of the essential oils recommended for use during pregnancy to 1 oz (30 ml) of base carrier oil. For babies and children see pages 37 and 54.

Should you have any adverse reaction — possibly itching, redness, or a rash developing — immediately wipe the blend off with carrier oil. Water is not effective, as oil and water don't mix. Refer to the list of essential oils on pages 62–63 for suitable oils for pregnancy, postnatal use, and for babies and children. Any list of oils and treatments should not be considered as total guidance. Consult your medical practitioner and your aromatherapist.

Essential oils for pregnancy

Pregnancy is a time of physical and emotional change, and essential oils can help you cope with the demands that are being made on you. In addition to using essential oils in massage blends, you can add the oils to the bath or room vaporizer to help relieve pain, fatigue and stress. It is best to consult a professional aromatherapist and always seek the advice of your doctor or midwife before using essential oils.

There are many benefits of aromatherapy during pregnancy and birth, especially in dealing with the stresses of pregnancy and labor and with postnatal recuperation. They can also help enhance the joys of this very special time.

There are some essential oils which should be avoided during pregnancy and others which should not be used during the first three or four months (see page 60). Be cautious; use low doses and consult a qualified aromatherapist.

For the birthing room use essential oils in massage and compresses for pain relief. Cool compresses wiped on the forehead and face between contractions will cool and relax. Hot compresses are occasionally used on the back only. Add your chosen essential oils to hot water in a bowl or in a vaporizer to release soothing fragrances into the room.

To improve the value of essential oils used in the bath dilute the oils first in 2 teaspoons (10 ml) of carrier oil, whole milk or pure cream. Get yourself wet then add the oil by swishing it through the water.

Edema (fluid retention)

Adequate rest is important during the latter part of the pregnancy. Swollen feet and legs, especially during the summer months can be very uncomfortable. When sitting always elevate your legs. Several short rests throughout the day are more beneficial than one longer one. Try a cool compress with lavender on the feet or massage the legs with a blend containing lavender and geranium.

Heartburn

Sandalwood, tangerine, mandarin, lemon or orange essential oils can be used as an inhalation by putting 2–3 drops of one oil in a basin of hot water and breathing deeply. Otherwise, use 2 drops of one of the oils mixed into 1 oz (30 ml) carrier oil and apply it in a clockwise movement over the abdominal area, circling right up to the ribs.

Hemorrhoids

Mix not more than two drops each of geranium and cypress oils in a non-petroleum lubricating jelly such as KY jelly which can be obtained from any pharmacy. Apply topically to the affected area. Use only once the pregnancy is secure, usually from about five months.

Insomnia

Before bed relax in a warm bath with lavender oil (approximately 5 drops for a standard bath). Dilute the oil in a teaspoon of carrier oil and mix well into the water. Place a rubber mat in the bath to avoid slipping. If possible get your partner to massage your neck and shoulders to soothe away the tiredness.

A few drops of a calming oil like chamomile or lavender used in a burner or diffused from a bowl of boiling water and placed in the bedroom overnight will improve your ability to sleep and to awake refreshed.

Oils to avoid during pregnancy

- angelica
- aniseed
- arnica
- basil
- birch
- camphor
- caraway
- carrot
- cedarwood
- cinnamon
- clary sage
- clove
- fennel
- hyssop
- jasmine
- juniper
- marjoram
- melissa
- mint
- mugwort
- myrrh
- nutmeg
- oregano
- pennyroyal
- rosemary
- rosewood
- sage
- sassafras
- tarragon
- thuja
- thyme
- wintergreen

Nausea

Some women find relief by sipping ginger tea. Make this by using fresh root ginger, sliced into coin sized pieces and steeped in boiling water for a few minutes. Peppermint or other herbal teas may be of assistance. If it can be arranged, it is beneficial to have these drinks before rising.

A few drops of peppermint or lemon essential oils placed on a handkerchief or tissue or used in a burner overnight or diffused from a bowl of boiling water may help prevent or relieve morning sickness.

Varicose veins

Gently stroke with the fingertips — do not massage — working up towards the thighs using a blend of geranium and cypress oils. Although not usually recommended for pregnancy, a weak blend of two drops of geranium and one drop of cypress in 2 teaspoons (10 ml) of carrier oil would be appropriate, provided that your pregnancy is secure.

Geranium oil will encourage circulation and cypress oil acts to tighten the stretched vein walls. If the veins are swollen and painful, consult your practitioner.

Each day elevate your legs to a position in which the feet are higher than your heart. This action helps to ease pressure on the distended veins and will assist the return of fluids to the heart.

Birthing room fragrances

See also the chapter on massage during childbirth.

During the lead-up to the birth, essential oils can be used in massage blends and hot compresses for pain relief. Cool compresses for the face and forehead between contractions will help cool and relax you. Add your chosen essential oils to a bowl of hot water or in a room vaporizer, to release soothing fragrances in the room.

Use about 6–8 drops of your chosen essential oils in a vaporizer to create the atmosphere you prefer for the birthing room. Lavender and tangerine will be calming and relaxing, frankincense will help alleviate any fears and will help slow and relax your breathing, and lemon and tea tree will freshen and disinfect the room.

Childbirth massage blends

These blends are 2 oz (50 ml) of base carrier oil mixed with 15–25 drops total of essential oils.
• Latent phase ("pre-labor") – frankincense 10 drops, sandalwood 5 drops, orange 5 drops.
• First stage – 20 drops lavender and 5 drops tangerine. A massage to the lower back with this blend will be calming and balancing to the nervous system.
• Second stage – 5 drops sandalwood and 15 drops lavender; or 15 drops clary sage, 5 drops rose and 5 drops ylang ylang.
• After the birth – In our view, no massage should be given until *after* the placenta is expelled.

Postnatal blends

See also the chapter on postnatal massage. Neroli, rose, chamomile and lavender are useful for postnatal massage. For healing the perineum, lavender, cypress and juniper are recommended. For soothing the breasts, chamomile and lavender are useful oils.

For the "baby blues" — caused by the changing hormone levels after the birth — have an aromatic bath or massage to lift your spirits and give yourself some time to relax.

Try a blend of one or two of the following oils:
• Uplifting – bergamot, lemon, neroli, orange
• Grounding – frankincense, lavender, sandalwood, ylang ylang
• Balancing – geranium, rose

If you are breastfeeding, greater care will be needed in the choice of which essential oils you use. Be careful to always thoroughly cleanse the breasts so that the baby never ingests the essential oil.

Aromatherapy for babies and children

Aromatherapy makes bathtime enjoyable, calming and comforting for children. It will help form relaxed sleeping habits and make their nights, and yours, stress-free.

Children respond well to the gentle nature of aromatherapy. The fragrance is appealing, and a child's immune system can be effectively assisted with the appropriate essential oils. A couple of drops of soothing chamomile or lavender in a bath or room vaporizer can calm an over-excited or irritable child, and help treat upset stomachs, rashes and other childhood illnesses. When bathing or changing a young child it is easy to extend the contact to a gentle aromatherapy massage. See the chapters on baby massage and massaging children.

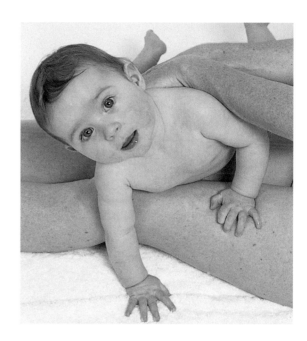

Although the use of aromatherapy is valuable during pregnancy and postnatally for both mother and baby, worldwide many babies do not have access to this luxury. However, *touch* is vital to life. Left without touching, babies will not thrive and certainly will not achieve their potential. Thus, the message of this book is to massage your infant. In return, the massage giver gains balance and sensitivity and a greater ability to use both hands in a flowing, caring way.

ESSENTIAL OIL	BOTANICAL NAME	PROPERTIES	USES	SUITABILITY
Bergamot	*Citrus aurantium*	Uplifting, refreshing	Cystitis, skin irritations, stress, anxiety	Postnatal use, babies and children (if oil diffused in air)
Calendula	*Calendula officinalis*	Antiseptic, healing	Stretch marks, diaper rash skin irritations	Advanced pregnancy, babies and children
Chamomile, Roman	*Anthemis nobilis*	Calming, soothing, anti-inflammatory, very gentle	Nausea, postnatal breast care, diaper rash, dry skin, insomnia, morning sickness	Pregnancy, babies and children
Clary Sage	*Salvia sclarea*	Antispasmodic, astringent, euphoric, uplifting	Menstrual pain, premenstrual tension, dry skin, stress, anxiety, depression	Late stages of childbirth, postnatal use
Cypress	*Cupressus sempervirens*	Astringent, warming	Perineum healing, hemorrhoids, anxiety, tension	For pregnancy if secure after five months, postnatal use
Eucalyptus	*Eucalyptus radiata*	Antibacterial, antiviral, decongestant, energizing	Colds, fever, asthma, sinusitis, wounds, bronchitis	Babies and children (if oil diffused in air)
Fennel, sweet	*Foeniculum vulgare*	Diuretic, hormone balancer	Strengthens womb, stimulates lactation, cellulite, edema	Last weeks of pregnancy, postnatal use
Frankincense	*Boswellia carteri*	Relaxing, calming, healing, comforting	Labor, stress, fear	Advanced pregnancy
Geranium	*Pelargonium graveolens*	Antiseptic, uplifting, antidepressant, hormone balancer, stabilizing	Dermatitis, eczema, postnatal depression	Advanced pregnancy, childbirth, postnatal use
Hypericum	*Hypericum perforatum*	Anti-inflammatory, soothing	Stretch marks, skin irritation, nervous tension	Advanced pregnancy
Jasmine	*Jasminum officinale*	Uplifting, stimulating	Postnatal depression, uterine tonic, coughs, dry skin, dermatitis	Late stages of childbirth, postnatal use
Juniper	*Juniperus communis*	Diuretic, detoxifying	Perineum healing, stretch marks, constipation, cellulite, tension	Postnatal use
Lavender	*Lavandula officinalis* or *Lavandula angustifolia*	Antibacterial, antidepressant, soothing, calming, balancing, versatile	Headaches, pain, eczema, insomnia, diaper rash, postnatal breast care	Pregnancy, childbirth, postnatal use, babies and children

ESSENTIAL OIL	BOTANICAL NAME	PROPERTIES	USES	SUITABILITY
Lemon	*Citrus limonum*	Antiseptic, uplifting, cleansing, refreshing	Morning sickness, nausea, heartburn, colds, lymphatic tonic	Pregnancy, postnatal use, babies and children
Marjoram	*Origanum majorana*	Sedating, warming,	Insomnia, perineum healing	Postnatal use
Myrrh	*Commiphora myrrha*	Antifungal, antiseptic, anti-inflammatory, cooling	Diaper rash, thrush, skin care	Postnatal use, older babies and children
Neroli	*Citrus aurantium*	Soothing, balancing, healing, calming	Dry skin, scars, circulation, stretch marks, stress, anxiety	Pregnancy, postnatal use
Orange	*Citrus sinensis*	Uplifting, calming	Skin care, stress, insomnia, heartburn, lymphatic tonic, anxiety	Pregnancy, babies and children (if oil diffused in air)
Peppermint	*Mentha piperita*	Antibacterial, analgesic, decongestant, antispasmodic	Morning sickness, nausea, headaches, indigestion	Late stages of pregnancy
Petitgrain	*Citrus aurantium*	Antidepressant, uplifting, refreshing	Skin care, insomnia, stress, inexpensive substitute for neroli	Pregnancy, postnatal use
Rose	*Rosa damascena* or *Rosa centifolia*	Antiseptic, anti-inflammatory, antidepressant, soothing, uplifting, hormone balancer	Dry skin, strengthens womb, tension, nausea	Last weeks of pregnancy, childbirth, postnatal use
Rosewood	*Aniba rosaeodora*	Antiseptic, tonic, sedative, calming	Nervous tension, anxiety, stress, tiredness, dry skin	Later stages of childbirth
Sandalwood	*Santalum album*	Healing, sedative, relaxing, warming	Irritated skin, rashes, nausea heartburn, diarrhea, colds, diaper rash	Pregnancy, childbirth, postnatal use, babies and children
Tangerine or Mandarin	*Citrus reticulata* or *Citrus noblis*	Soothing, calming, uplifting	Stretch marks, insomnia, nervous tension, scars	Pregnancy, childbirth, babies and children
Ylang Ylang	*Cananga odorata*	Antidepressant, relaxing, sedative, calming	Skin care, insomnia, hypertension, palpitations, tension	Advanced pregnancy

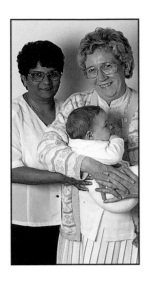

ABOUT THE AUTHORS

SUSIE NANAYAKKARA R.N., C.M., Dip Aromatherapy (Aus) trained in the United Kingdom and worked at Royal Berkshire Hospital, Reading, and in the peripheral hospitals for fifteen years. The last five years of that time Susie was a Senior Midwife. Currently she is working as a Clinical Nurse Specialist in the Birth Unit of Auburn District Hospital, Sydney, Australia, and has implemented the use of aromatherapy in the Birth Unit.

ROMA TURNER Dip. Aromatherapy and Remedial Therapies was a nurse and then spent many years as a school-teacher. Besides training sporting teams and teaching swimming in schools, Roma looked after the first aid for any serious cases that occurred.

Having completed courses in various types of massage, Roma, with her husband Phillip, started a college in the early 1980s which teaches massage, thus their theoretical knowledge is supported by their work as masseurs. Active in the professional associations, Roma was President of the Association of Remedial Masseurs for many years and is on the Management Committee of The Australian Traditional-Medicine Society.

First published in Great Britain in 1996
by Chancellor Press
a division of Reed Consumer Books
Michelin House, 81 Fulham Rd, London SW3 6RB

Produced by Lansdowne Publishing Pty Ltd
Level 5, 70 George Street, Sydney, NSW, 2000, Australia

© Copyright: Lansdowne Publishing Pty Ltd

Photographer: Andre Martin
Models: Lucille Pearson, Deborah Nixon, Niki Barnes,
Pablo and Benito Martin, Roslyn Burton, Nicholas Szentkuti

Set in Caslon 540 Roman on Quark Xpress
Printed in Singapore by Tien Wah Press (Pte) Ltd

ISBN 1 85152 916 0

We recommend that the techniques and ideas presented in this book should
be supported by medical advice from your doctor or midwife at the individual
level. Advice regarding oils should be sought from a qualified aromatherapist.
The use of any of the information given is the reader's sole choice and risk.